1973

89953

HQ
766.5   Lindemann, Con-
.U5   stance
L55
1975   Birth control and
                 unmarried young
                 women

BIRTH CONTROL
and
Unmarried Young Women

BIRTH CONTROL
and
Unmarried Young Women

CONSTANCE LINDEMANN, Dr.P.H.

Assistant Professor, College of Nursing
Arizona State University
Tempe, Arizona

SPRINGER PUBLISHING COMPANY

NEW YORK

SPRINGER PUBLISHING COMPANY, INC.
200 Park Avenue South, New York, N. Y. 10003

Library of Congress Cataloging in Publication Data

Lindemann, Constance, 1923-
Birth control and unmarried young women.

Bibliography: p.
1. Birth control–United States.   2. Single women.
3. Adolescent girls.   4. Youth–Sexual behavior.
I. Title.   [DNLM: 1. Family planning. HQ766 L743b]
HQ766.5.U5L55   301.41'75'33   74-14769
ISBN 0-8261-1700-7

Preface

My objective in this book is to present in readable, useful form the findings of my research on the problem of preventing unwanted pregnancy in young unmarried women. I believe this information will be of value to young women who face or may face this problem, as well as to behavioral scientists, health practitioners—physicians, nurses, social workers, and others in the field of health planning—and to interested laymen. Since the audience consists of so many varied groups, a style and language was chosen that would be comprehensible to all of them. The content itself is based on research done at the School of Public Health at the University of California at Los Angeles.

I wish to thank the Fairfax Avenue Free Clinic and the Public Health Youth Clinics of Los Angeles, and the National Center for Health Services Research and Development which provided funds that allowed me to conduct these studies (grant # 8 TO1-HS00016). I appreciate especially the suggestions, support, and guidance of Dr. Leo G. Reeder of the School of Public Health at the University of California at Los Angeles; Dr. William Morris, now at the University of Colorado Medical School; and Dr. Barney G. Glaser of the University of California Medical Center at San Francisco. Particularly, I want to thank the young women I observed and talked to in the course of this research—young women who were struggling with the problem of avoiding pregnancy and who shared their experiences with me.

Tempe, Arizona
June, 1974

Contents

CHAPTER I

Prescription for Preventing Pregnancy

Our most pressing problem is preventing unwanted pregnancies and births among teen-agers, not helping them to have well-adjusted sex lives," said the director of a health department's youth clinics (*Family Planning Digest,* 1972). Preventing pregnancy is also a pressing problem for many a young woman, but adjusting to her sex life and relating it to other aspects of life are also part of her problem.

Confronted with the necessity for making these adjustments, a girl may do any one of a number of things about birth control: she may do nothing at all, or she may use a method of contraception—effective or ineffective, and she may do either of these things consistently or inconsistently; or she may prepare herself with a birth control method before she has sexual intercourse for the first time or not until afterwards. She may stick to one of these types of behavior or change from one to another. And if, as a consequence of any of these behaviors, she becomes pregnant, she may still avoid having a baby by choosing to have an abortion.

THE PROCESS OF SOLVING THE PROBLEM

In their attempts to find a means of avoiding pregnancy, young unmarried women usually go through three stages: the natural stage, the peer stage, and the expert stage. During the

9

natural stage they do nothing about contraception; during the peer stage they get information from peers and experiment with various methods and patterns of birth control use; and during the expert stage they consult a professional or paraprofessional in the family planning field. These stages of birth control behavior are steps in a social process that evolves as young women respond to their perceptions and interpretations of the social environment. Since there have been no ground rules, so to speak, no established norm for birth control behavior, the young women themselves have had to choose their own birth control behavior patterns in the course of their day-to-day experiences. I call this process the *birth control prescription process.* As it evolves, the prescription for the pregnancy problem changes, and, as the prescription changes, it, in turn, changes the very problem for which the prescription was found. The process, then, involves repeatedly finding new prescriptions to fit changing conditions.

The girl-boy relationship, parents, the expert, patterns of sexual activity, levels of awareness, the girl's readiness to disclose her sexual activity to others, and her perceptions of the risks and benefits of contraception are all more or less influential at varying points in the three stages of the process. The stages and the behaviors and conditions that influence movement in the process are described in Chapters II, III, and IV.

Movement from one stage to another can be either progressive or retrogressive, depending on what conditions prevail. Some patterns of movement enhance the chances of pregnancy and some lower it. Only the pattern that consists of using a 100-percent effective contraceptive at all times provides the maximum protection against the risk of pregnancy. At the present time, this pattern is the one least often followed. Patterns of movement is the subject of Chapter V.

Although birth control methods become more effective with each succeeding stage of the prescription process, pregnancy may occur despite a woman's utmost efforts to prevent it. When it does occur, abortion is often used to terminate it. Pregnancy and abortion as facilitators or propellants in the birth control prescription process or as consequences of the process are discussed in Chapter VI.

A SUBSTANTIVE THEORY OF
BIRTH CONTROL BEHAVIOR

The prescription process helps to explain much of the behavior of sexually active, young, single women. It answers the questions parents, professional family planners, government officials, and other concerned members of society ask: Why are there so many out-of-wedlock pregnancies? Why is abortion so frequently used rather than contraception? Why, if young, unmarried people are having sexual intercourse, don't they *use* something? Perhaps of even greater importance, understanding the process may help young women, who are often surprised and anguished at an unanticipated pregnancy, to understand their own behavior.

In seeking the answers to these questions, I became a birth control counselor at a free clinic. In addition, I counseled, lectured, and led "rap sessions" at many free and public health clinics and high schools and colleges throughout the Los Angeles metropolitan area. While doing this, I observed, interviewed and questioned, individually and in groups, some 2,500 young women. This research is described in Chapter VIII. The qualitative data collected in the course of questioning and counseling these young women were the source from which the theory of the birth control prescription process was derived. This is a substantive theory of the birth control behavior of young, single women. The method used was the grounded theory method, described in *The Discovery of Grounded Theory* (Glaser and Strauss, 1967). The outstanding merit of this method is that it affords a systematic way of collecting and analyzing qualitative data. The method is briefly explained in Chapter VIII.

The practical and theoretical implications of the birth control prescription process theory are discussed in Chapters VII and IX.

CHAPTER II

The Natural Stage

When a young girl starts to have sexual intercourse, she is beset by problems arising from her new behavior and a new kind of relationship. Although her most pressing problem, whether she is aware of it or not, is how to obtain an effective birth control method, the likelihood is that she will do nothing about it. This "do nothing" behavior characterizes the first stage, the natural stage, of the prescription process, and results from various conditions present in the social environment at this point in the young woman's life.

PATTERNS OF SEXUAL BEHAVIOR

The first of these conditions is that, in the nonmarital context, patterns of sexual behavior are in a state of constant flux. This condition of constant flux is the basis for a girl's behavior and movement in the natural stage of the prescription process, a stage in which the very nature of sexual activity is not conducive to the use of contraceptives.

There are several dimensions of sexual activity in the sexual behavior of girls at this stage that influence movement in the prescription process. These dimensions are the *unpredictability* of coitus, a belief in the *spontaneity* and *naturalness* of sex, the *infrequency* of coitus, the *type* of sexual activity, and the *duration* of sexual activity.

13

Unpredictability

In the early phases of sexual activity the occurrence of coitus is unpredictable. As Lowry (1969) and Eastman (1972) have indicated, there is an enormous range of circumstances surrounding the first coitus. Contraceptives are not used because intercourse is unplanned and unanticipated. As one girl said:

> I didn't have birth control because I had never been in that situation. I will be more careful after this [abortion], and if I ever got in the same situation I'd scream because I didn't do this [prepare with a birth control method].

Coitus does not necessarily become more predictable after the first experience. Subsequent experiences may also be unexpected and this may happen repeatedly. This was clearly expressed by a young woman who said:

> Many times you don't know when it's going to happen. The first time I didn't think I would [have sexual intercourse]. You keep thinking that for a while until you decide. I wouldn't expect that I would be doing it each time.

This state of unpredictability, of not knowing if and when sexual intercourse will take place, inhibits the use of birth control not only in the natural stage but all through the prescription process. When there are no immediate and concrete prospects of sexual intercourse, there is reluctance to prepare with a birth control method:

> I'll take a chance the first time. I couldn't carry foam or a condom around all the time. I wouldn't take pills because I might have to take them too long before I have sex.*

*All unascribed quotations are remarks made by young women in the course of the research.

The three components of unpredictability—time, place, and partner—are also components of planning. One, two, or all of them may be unpredictable. There may be no suitable place available for sexual activity, and if a place can be found the time may be unpredictable: "Sometimes I don't know when my boyfriend is coming over." If there is no present involvement with a partner, there is no way to predict with whom a sexual involvement will develop. As one girl said:

> I'm the type that has to be involved with someone. It wasn't until I got involved that I knew it would be a continuing thing and I'd better get birth control.

Casual encounters with new people or having more than one sexual partner are additional kinds of partner unpredictability. This is illustrated by a young woman who said, "I don't plan my sexual relationships. I take my chances."

Thus, unpredictability is a condition of nonmarital sexual activity. It influences movement all through the prescription process. As sex becomes more predictable, changes occur in birth control behavior that affect movement in the prescription process.

Spontaneity and Naturalness

The second dimension of sexual activity that influences behavior in the natural stage is the belief that sex should be spontaneous or "natural."

> Sex is better if it's natural. Birth control is artificial. Getting birth control would shatter romantic ideas. I didn't like the idea of birth control because sex should be spontaneous.

As Hardin (1966) points outs, "It is one of the psychological weaknesses of contraception that it requires the rational anticipation of an abrogation of reason—which affronts both the logician and the poet in us." The belief that sex should be spontaneous has a direct effect on behavior and it also reinforces unpredictability by giving it a rationale. In the natural stage of the prescription process it is a rationale for avoiding birth control, while in later stages it manifests itself in the search for a birth control method that simulates nature.

Infrequency

The third dimension of sexual activity that inhibits progress in the prescription process is the infrequency of coitus. One young woman said:

After the first time I had sex I didn't do it again for a year. After the second time it was very infrequent.

Another young woman said:

I went for seven years between the first time I had sex and the next time. Then about once a month for six times.

One effect of infrequent coitus is that, if a young woman has thoughts about birth control, they only occur when she has intercourse and soon dissipate. Another effect is that chances of pregnancy seem minimal when sexual intercourse is infrequent, so contraceptives are not used: "I was scared, but it [coitus] was so rare." Indeed, the perception that chances of pregnancy are minimized by infrequent intercourse is borne out in statistical studies (Barret and Marshall, 1969). The infrequency of coitus at this stage means it is not part of a regular pattern of behavior. This also contributes to the difficulty of anticipating and predicting.

Frequency of coitus is a major influence on movement in

the prescription process and has a direct impact on birth control behavior in all three stages.

Type

The fourth dimension of sexual activity that influences movement in the prescription process is the type of sexual activity a girl engages in. A girl who changed from homosexual to heterosexual relationships said that because she had been "messing around with women" she was not prepared with a birth control method when she subsequently had sexual intercourse with a man. She got pregnant. Encouraging homosexuality has been proposed as a possible measure to reduce fertility (Elliot, et al., 1970), but this example indicates that it may not have the desired effect.

Duration

The length of time since first coitus (duration of sexual activity) is the final dimension that affects movement in the process. Although the likelihood that a birth control method will be used increases as the time a girl has been sexually active increases, the opposite effect may also occur. Nonuse of contraception for a period of time will reinforce the notion that pregnancy will not occur. This is revealed in such statements as: "I'm afraid of getting pregnant. I don't think it could happen to me. I've been having sex for two years. So far it hasn't." This conclusion may also be based on observing others: "Some girls have had sex and didn't get pregnant." Indeed, according to Montagu (1969), it is possible for young women to be sterile for up to seven years after the start of menstruation.

The five dimensions of sexual activity—unpredictability, spontaneity, infrequency, type, and duration—influence the sexual behavior of young women in the natural stage, but, as has already been indicated, their effects do not end with the natural stage and some of them have a major influence on movement in later stages of the process.

THE PROBLEM OF AWARENESS

The second condition influencing behavior at the natural stage is the degree of the young woman's awareness of the need for birth control. Adoption of new sex behavior does not automatically bring this awareness with it; changes first have to take place in the girl's awareness of her sex behavior and of the possibility of pregnancy. A new self-concept has to be acquired that includes this new behavior and possibility. The girl has to learn to define herself as sexually active, capable of reproduction, and in need of contraception.

The requirements for adopting a new role and new self-concept are: (1) a desire for identity change, (2) an understanding of what needs to be changed, (3) a knowledge of the roles and styles of performance appropriate to the new identity, (4) a commitment to making the change, (5) the physical and emotional capacity to make the change, (6) recognition and acceptance by others, and finally, (7) complete acceptance of the new identity (Goodenough, 1963). To assume a new role an individual must abandon what she once was and commit herself to the conception of self that the new role requires (Cogswell, 1967).

There is a conflict between the requirements of a sexually active, unmarried girl and what society customarily allows to a girl of her age and marital status. The conflict is manifested in the girl herself and in her interactions with key members of the social structure—her boyfriend, her parents, and professionals in the field of birth control. This conflict between the girl's requirements and what she is allowed appears again and again. It is the source of much of the behavior that occurs in the course of the prescription process.

Awareness of Sexual Behavior

There are varying levels of awareness of sexual behavior. In extreme cases, it is possible to be completely unaware of having had sexual intercourse. This may occur when trauma is associated with the act or when the stakes are very high. One girl had no awareness that she had had sexual intercourse and denied the possibility of being pregnant up until the time her baby was born. The pregnancy meant forever losing her chance to continue in school, which was the only way to escape the cycle of poverty in her country. There was no possibility of abortion.

Total lack of awareness can also occur when the girl is under the influence of alcohol or drugs. An 18-year-old burst into tears when her pregnancy test proved positive and wailed, "I didn't even know I had it [sexual intercourse]." She and her 17-year-old high school sweetheart had "had a little wine." An older girl said that all four of her children were conceived when she was under the influence of drugs.

At the other extreme is full awareness—the girl fully realizes the implications and consequences of her sexual behavior and understands the need for a birth control method. This makes it possible for her to prepare with a method either before sexual intercourse takes place for the first time or immediately afterwards. A young girl who came to the clinic for information before having sexual intercourse said: "Some people are more aware. That's just the way they are, the way they were brought up." Such girls skip the natural stage of the prescription process completely.

But these extremes are not typical and the level of awareness at the natural stage falls somewhere between them. For instance, there may be a high level of awareness around the time that intercourse occurs, but little or none in the intervals between. Or there may be a drift into sexual activity on a low level of awareness and continuation in this manner for some time. In either case, intercourse is still an accident, a fluke. The girl's new sexual behavior has not yet become integrated into her standard repertoire of behaviors. In the words of Simone de Beauvior (1952), the young woman's "actions retain a theoretical cast that makes them as unreal as the fantasies in which others anticipate the future." Under these circumstances a new self-concept is hard to maintain. By contributing to this state of affairs, unpredictable and infrequent sexual activity reinforces low awareness.

Awareness of the Possibility of Becoming Pregnant

At the natural stage there is generally a low level of awareness of the possibility of becoming pregnant:

> I don't remember if I thought about getting pregnant. I don't know why, but it just didn't bother me that much.

Pregnancy, like sexual behavior, is not part of the girl's self-concept; she feels no identification with it:

> It was just not possible for it to happen to me. I just didn't believe I could get pregnant.

Or, as another girl said:

> It just couldn't happen to me. I've read about birth control. I knew about contraceptives. I knew the statistics. I could have prepared for it. I knew it was easy to get pregnant, but not for me.[1]

---

[1] Lack of awareness of the possibility of events occurring is not confined to the possibility of becoming pregnant; it also occurs in other areas of life. A young woman reporter who was the victim of a mugging used almost the same words as the girl in the example above to describe her attitude: "There were 14,407 robberies in the District of Columbia last year. I read the statistics. I just never thought I'd become one" (Cimons, 1971).

Levels of awareness about the possibility of becoming pregnant vary, as do those about sexual behavior. In contrast to the girl who wasn't bothered is the girl who, after having intercourse for the first itme, "cried every day for two weeks" until her menstrual period came. The more aware girl will be apt to acquire a birth control method sooner, although infrequent and unpredictable coitus may still act as a deterrent.

Awareness of the Need for Contraception

The first prerequisite in using contraception is awareness that there are ways to prevent conception. It is possible to be totally ignorant of birth control methods:

> I was young. I didn't know about pills or foam or anything. My family was pretty poor. They didn't tell me. Younger kids need to know. It will cut down illegitimacy.

But knowing about birth control methods is not synonymous with being aware of the need for them. The problem is that, while sexual activity can continue on a low level of awareness, using birth control requires a conscious, fully aware act: "Sex is natural. For birth control you need education." Just as the possibility of becoming pregnant is not part of the self-concept, neither is the possibility of using contraceptives:

> I kept saying I'd better go [to get a contraceptive], but I just never did. I knew about the different methods and how they worked, but the thought of me doing it was weird.

Acquiring a birth control method competes with other things that need attention, so in spite of a girl's awareness of the need for it, it may sometimes be neglected:

I went for a year without birth control and nothing happened. I think I would do the same if I had it to do over. That's how I am. I don't worry about things until they happen. There are so many hassles going on in your mind that even though these are the most important they get lost.[2]

Growing Awareness

Awareness increases in the natural stage as it does all through the prescription process. It may take place slowly and gradually or rapidly and suddenly. Gradual growth of awareness has quantitative and qualitative components. Quantitatively, it is the result of more sexual experience in terms of the number and frequency of incidences of coitus and of the length of time since the first sexual experience. The more sexually active a girl is, the greater are her chances of becoming aware of her behavior and of her need for birth control. Thus, frequency and duration of sexual activity have a marked effect on awareness. Qualitatively, it is manifested in a greater degree of comfort and familiarity with her new sexual role.

Rapid and sudden growth of awareness occurs after an encounter with pregnancy. This may happen when there is a pregnancy scare due to a late menstrual period, when a friend gets pregnant, or when the girl herself gets pregnant.

As awareness grows, the girl becomes clearer about the implications of her sexual behavior. This is illustrated by a young woman who said:

I didn't get birth control the first time because I was young and didn't realize how important it was. I realized the necessity because of my present boyfriend—the one I guess I'm going to be with the rest of my life. I realized I have to make it on my own, married or whatever—have got to get myself together before I have children.

---

[2] This is similar to the low priority that people with low incomes give to health care, due to the many other problems that must take precedence, according to Rainwater (1968). Competition among various needs is also noted in Mechanic's (1968) model for help-seeking behavior.

Growing awareness exerts a constant pressure toward progress in the prescription process, and, in turn, experience in the prescription process increases awareness. Thus, awareness and the prescription process are in constant interaction with each other. As awareness increases, new behaviors are chosen to resolve problems. The same factors may be present; the difference in behavior is due to different interpretation of them. With greater awareness the ill-defined concept of self is replaced with a clearer definition of self as a sexually active person capable of reproduction and in need of birth control. The factors of awareness and ill-defined self-concept are present in other aspects of the natural stage. These will be discussed in the section on the boy-girl relationship.

DECIDING WHAT TO DO

Another condition typical of the natural stage of the prescription process is the young woman's indecision about when to acquire a birth control method. Should she acquire it in anticipation of her first sexual experience even though she has no immediate prospects of having sex? Should she get it after a relationship with a boy has begun, but before the first coitus? Or should she wait until one or more sexual experiences have taken place? As one girl put it, "Seems dumb to get it before. Then again, it seems smart."

American adolescents are oriented toward an ideal of premarital chastity, but at the same time they are continuously bombarded with sexual stimuli. Hence, there is a conflict between the ideal and the reality, and the adolescent must choose between observing standards and feeling frustrated and cheated or violating them and feeling guilty and risking social disapproval (Muuss, 1970). Indecision about when to get a birth control method really reflects this ambivalence:

> If you get birth control first it's like you're condoning it, and you've always been told it's bad.

And indecision about sex inhibits the acquisition of a contraceptive:

> You're so busy talking about whether or not to have
> sex that you forget about birth control, and by the
> time you do have sex you don't have any birth
> control.

Commitment to Sex

Indecision does not necessarily end after sexual intercourse has occurred. Having sexual intercourse once or even many times does not mean *commitment to sex*. A girl who had been having sexual intercourse for three months without a contraceptive said:

> I thought about it a lot of times. I was not sure of the
> situation I was in and whether it would be a good
> thing. I wasn't sure whether I wanted to take a
> contraceptive, not because of the birth control itself,
> but because of the sex.

Doing something that has been described as "bad" fosters guilt feelings, but the feelings of guilt do not deter sexual activity. They do deter getting a birth control method. According to Reiss (1970), people must learn to view premarital intercourse as ethically acceptable before they can use an oral contraceptive successfully. One pregnant girl who was seeking abortion information explained that she had not been using a contraceptive because "I couldn't get the pill without telling my parents. I would feel guilty about taking the pill behind their back."

Indecision and guilt about sex get focused on birth control. Sexual activity is the background to a commitment to sex, but it does not *mean* commitment, just the possibility of commitment. It is the decision to get a birth control method that really means commitment to sex. This was expressed clearly by a girl who had not yet had intercourse:

I've been thinking about it, the pill, that is. I've been persuaded by my boyfriend that I ought to get it. Haven't made up my mind yet. I won't get the pill tonight. I'll discuss it with my boyfriend again. If I get the pill I'm open. Then I can screw around when I want. I like the idea of having drawbacks.

In cases like this, sometimes a girl does choose abstention rather than contraception, but resolutions of abstention are easily broken. The failure rate of abstinence as a birth control method is considerable. Even young women who are determined to remain virginal until their wedding day may find it difficult to remain abstinent. Girls who are opposed to premarital sex sometimes end up having it, just as do girls who favor it or are ambivalent about it. In one such case, an abortion request came from the sister of a young, unmarried, pregnant woman. The community health aide who was supervising the woman's case, in keeping with her policy of talking to siblings about sex and birth control, had talked with the sister about these things on several occasions. Although the girl insisted that she did not need a birth control method because she intended to remain a virgin until she was married, she did have intercourse, got pregnant, and asked for an abortion.

The fact that it is not sexual intercourse but obtaining a method of birth control that shows a commitment to sex means there is a delay in getting a birth control method until after intercourse has taken place. Basic to the natural stage is this seeming paradox of not using contraceptives when pregnancy is unwanted. The lack of commitment to sex explains this paradox.

THE BOY-GIRL RELATIONSHIP

Many aspects of the relationship between the girl and boy condition movement in the prescription process. Three of these are: the definition of the relationship; changing standards of sexual behavior; and the boy's level of awareness.

Definition of the Relationship

Ability to define the relationship is a contributing factor to birth control behavior. A prevalent hypothesis about why girls don't use contraceptives is that they want to promote marriage (Pohlman, 1967). They define the relationship as one that will lead to marriage. This is true in some cases. One young woman said she had not used a contraceptive in the earlier stages of her relationship with her boyfriend because:

> I didn't care if I got pregnant then. We could have handled it. We could have gotten married. But now that we are getting married and will be having sex more frequently, I need something.

As a matter of fact, studies show that most girls do not marry the father of babies conceived out of wedlock. "Most of the unmarried mothers stated that they did not plan to see the putative fathers after delivery," say Kinch, et al. (1969).

There is evidence that birth control is used or not used to accomplish other ends regarding relationships with the opposite sex. A girl who had never used contraceptives said:

> I'm going with somebody now and I don't want anything to interfere with the relationship. I think a pregnancy would interfere with it, so I need a contraceptive.

A 26-year-old woman who had been casual about the use of contraceptives and was now pregnant insisted upon having an abortion because, she said, she had no intention of ever marrying and did not want children. One girl, who defined herself as the "aggressor" in her relationship with her boyfriend, said that since he hadn't "done anything" about preparing for sex, she prepared with foam for their first sexual experience.

Such motives are not confined to young women. One

young man said he would not mind getting involved in a pregnancy situation "with a chick I cared something about, but if it were a chick I didn't care about I would not want to get involved, so then I would be more careful about using something." Another young man deliberately refrained from using a birth control method because "that was the girl I wanted to marry." The point is that promoting marriage by not using birth control is only one of a number of possible behaviors. The choice depends on what one wants in a relationship with the opposite sex. When there is a clear definition a decision will be made about birth control and it will be used or not used according to the needs of the situation. When the conditions of the relationship are not well defined and there is a choice between use and nonuse, the tendency is toward nonuse. This behavior is similar to that which occurs when there is a lack of awareness and an ill-defined self-concept. In the natural stage definitions are not clear and, given the other factors that inhibit progress, the tendency is to be lax about birth control.

Changing Standards

Another factor in relationships between girls and boys that influences birth control behavior is the change in standards of sexual behavior. The old double standard (Reiss, 1967) meant that boys could be sexually active before marriage but girls were obliged to remain virginal until their wedding night. Now girls are sexually active as well. New twists on the double standard come out when questions like these are asked: Who is supposed to start the talk about birth control? Who decides whether to use it? Who initiates the action to get birth control? Who should provide it?

When old social standards break down and new ones evolve, new forms of communication and behavior are needed (Daniels, 1971). At this time, there are no customs, rules of thumb, or norms about what to expect in terms of birth control in the relation between a girl and boy, and no etiquette or standardized way to communicate about it. There is no customary way for the girl who is not prepared with a contraceptive to ask the boy if he has one. Each may arrive at the scene with different expectations and, because of the lack of an etiquette, may not be able to communicate or check out the situation. The boy may expect that the girl is taking an oral contraceptive. The girl, on the other hand, may expect something else: "The guy is supposed to have something. After all, if he takes you out. . . ." Communication on the physical level does not guarantee communication on the level that is necessary for checking about birth control. This may be true even when there is a high level of knowledge about the subject. A 22-year-old graduate student in health education, for instance, said that he did not always broach the subject because it was a "clumsy question."

Communication is affected by the nature of the involvement between the boy and girl. When asked why, in such an intimate situation, it is so difficult to ask about birth control, someone in a rap session replied, "That's the trouble, it's not intimate."

Another twist on the double standard is evident when initiating the action of acquiring a birth control method. When sexual intercourse is anticipated or is already taking place, the girl may fear the boy will think she has loose morals if she is prepared with a method or initiates action to acquire one. So it is preferable for the idea to come from the boy: "I waited for my boyfriend to say something. It was his idea that I come to the clinic." To these young people it is the display of knowledge or experience about birth control that means loose morals, not having sex! Here again, as in commitment to sex and as in ambivalence about sexual activity and birth control, the question of looseness gets focused not on sexual intercourse itself but on birth control.

The Boy's Level of Awareness

The boy's level of awareness of the problem of preventing pregnancy is a contributing factor in the prescription process. A young man who came to a rap session with his girlfriend said:

> I was probably getting into a hard trip. I had been thinking, "Why don't we prepare for it instead of thinking it won't happen?" This occurred to me in between the times I saw her. I then discussed it with her at the first opportunity.

Growth of awareness takes place in the boy in much the same way as in the girl, and the problems of definition, ambivalence, awareness, and expectations that are found in the girl are similarly found in the boy, as well as in the nexus between them. These problems also arise in interactions with others in the course of the prescription process.

WHO TO TURN TO FOR HELP

Another condition for behavior and movement in the birth control prescription process is the girl's perception of possible sources of help in solving the problem of preventing pregnancy.

Parents as a Resource

A girl cannot readily ask her parents about birth control. They are usually ambivalent about, if not downright opposed to, premarital sex. Even in families that have a permissive attitude toward premarital sex parents are not able to help their daughters plan for birth control in concrete terms. When it comes to what to do, where to go, and which method to use, the family doesn't tell and the girls don't ask. A birth control consultant told of the following incident, which occurred at a community meeting on overpopulation:

A woman kept asking why on earth these girls don't use anything. After the meeting she told me that she had been involved with three young girls in their efforts to obtain abortions and had gone with them to Tijuana [a popular place in Mexico for illegal abortions]. She just couldn't understand why they hadn't used contraception. Immediately she went on to say that she had not been able to discuss the subject with her own daughter despite the urging of her husband [who was obviously also reluctant]. The outcome was that her daughter was given an oral contraceptive by a physician to correct menstrual irregularity. The woman said she was greatly relieved by this.

This mother was absolved of responsibility for her daughter's birth control planning, and although she herself considered it a "cop out," she welcomed the intervention of a third party.

This reluctance to disclose and discuss sexual activity and birth control is widespread. It is not confined to cultures that have puritanical attitudes toward premarital sex or the kind of norms that prevail in the United States. Even in primitive societies where premarital sex is encouraged and provided for, where it is the prevailing norm, discussion about it does not take place between generations within a family. Mothers do not instruct or talk to their daughters about these matters. At the same time, they do not discourage or in any way exhibit negative attitudes toward their daughters' premarital sexual activities. Likewise, fathers do not instruct or talk to their sons about sex. There are other societal provisions for learning about and engaging in premarital sex. The matter is taken care of outside the parental family. There is apparently no rigid taboo that prohibits this discussion. Rather, it is a tacit agreement for the comfort of the members of the family (Malinoski, 1929).

In our society, even in permissive families, girls and parents are reluctant to discuss birth control in concrete, here-and-now terms. Girls find it is not possible for them to actually let their parents know when sexual intercourse is imminent. In an extreme case, a very young girl did not use foam, although it had been given to her by her mother. She was afraid to let her mother know that she was actually using it! Another girl had been having sexual intercourse for a month before her mother found out and sent her to a free clinic for a birth control method. In this case, it was the impetus from the parent that moved the girl into another stage of the prescription process. Although this is about the most permissive type of parental attitude, the girl still entered the prescription process at the natural stage and stayed there for a month. In most cases, this type of direct intervention is not forthcoming, even in permissive families. However, the permissive attitude does provide a setting and background for making faster progress in the prescription process, with the possibility of skipping the peer prescription stage and moving directly from the natural stage to the expert stage.

Reiss (1966) has maintained that, while "the presence of contraceptive information is not a major cause of coitus, the absence of it is a major cause of premarital pregnancy." But permissive parents who recognize that their daughter may have premarital sex do not want to appear to sanction it by offering information on birth control. They fear that this will be pushing the girl into premarital sex—that it will be a go-ahead sign. These parents will consider giving birth control information and advice at an early age, but concrete help only when sex is in the offing:

> I discussed sex and birth control with my daughters when they were 12 and 13. I did not want to just give them pills, but some girls develop a desire for sex at a much earlier age than others do, and I told them

when they felt they were at that point they should come to me and I would see to it that they got to a doctor for birth control.

But even in a case like this the girl has to initiate the procedure. Since she is reluctant to disclose her sexual activity, she may not initiate a discussion about birth control until she has been having sexual intercourse for some time. It is even more likely that she will not discuss it with her parents at all, but will solve the problem in some other manner after she has been in the natural stage for a time. One young woman had discussed birth control with her mother, who was a nurse. The mother was permissive about sex and told her if she even got pregnant to let her know. Yet this girl would not ask her mother about the diaphragm when she saw it at home, and her mother does not know she is having sex.

While some families will accept the fact that their daughter is having premarital sex, they may question the safety of oral contraceptives. For example, a 16-year-old girl obtained an oral contraceptive from her family doctor before her first sexual experience. This required a note from her parents. She felt free to raise the question with her mother. Her mother and sister took oral contraceptives. She said, "My mother does not object to sex, but does object to my going on pills so soon." In such cases, opposition to birth control is usually overcome and the parent, in recognition of the necessity of preventing pregnancy, gives her consent despite her objections.

The posture of parents in permissive families toward premarital sex and birth control indicates that ambivalence is not only manifested by the girls but also by their parents.

In most families premarital sex is completely unacceptable, and the girl is expected to abstain from sex until she is married. Under these conditions, there is no discussion, information, or advice on birth control methods. In one such family, a girl constantly approached her parents for discussion and help, but was rebuffed each time. The benefits of, and need for, such a discussion were not perceived by them. In many families, if the girl gets pregnant she is forgiven for that one mistake, but she is expected to abstain from further sexual activity until she is married. At the other extreme, she may be thrown out of the house or she may elect to leave so that her parents do not discover her plight. In most cases, the family becomes reconciled to the situation and the girl acquires a method of birth control after an abortion or the birth of a baby.

In a few families the emphasis is on the unacceptability of birth control, usually for religious reasons. As in the nonpermissive family, the girl is expected to abstain, and if she does get pregnant she is expected to abstain afterwards. The problems of abstinence as a birth control method have been discussed in a previous section. The result is often more than one pregnancy. In situations like this, it may take more than one pregnancy encounter to make progress in the prescription process.

In addition to not being able to use parents as a resource, the parent-daughter relationship is profoundly important in another way. It is necessary for the formation of a new self-concept to have it recognized and accepted by others, especially by key persons like parents (Goodenough, 1963). If the parents cannot do this, it will be difficult for their daughter to achieve a new self-concept.

School as a Resource

Since the parents cannot be used as a resource, the next most likely candidate is school. Some schools do not teach anything about sex or birth control at all. Others teach biology but not how to prevent pregnancy. Still others do include in their biology or health courses information on birth control methods and how they work, but they do not teach where to obtain contraceptives and how to gain access to an expert.

Although girls prefer the "peer group, school setting for

education in sexuality" (Thiebaux, 1972), most college adminis-
trations continue to ignore the need students have for birth
control information. As a result, the information is being
supplied by the students themselves via student printing presses
(Crist and Starnes, 1972). An example of this is the *Birth
Control Handbook* put out by the McGill Students' Society
(Cherniak and Feingold, 1970). In some high schools student
women's liberation groups have begun to bring birth control
education to the schools (*McCall's,* 1972). In many schools
faculty and/or parent groups are attempting to institute
programs in sex education, including birth control, but these
programs are under chronic attack by irate citizens (Kimmey,
1972).

Mass Media as a Resource

The mass media—newspaper, magazines, radio, television
and movies—are not fruitful sources of contraceptive information. "They don't advertise methods enough," said one girl who
had been pregnant. Very few girls report that they found out
about contraception or where to go for birth control services
from the mass media. Foam is sometimes discovered through
magazine or newspaper advertisements, and most ads advise that
it can be purchased at any drug store. There is some radio and
television advertising, but generally contraceptive information is
virtually absent from press, television, radio, and magazines:

> The media have shown reluctance to carry material
> advertising the availability of contraceptive services to
> the young and unmarried. (*Family Planning Digest,*
> 1972)

Even the "underground" press advertises abortion clinics and
services more consistently than it advertises birth prevention
services.

Actually, there is some question as to whether the mass media are good resources for birth control information. A study conducted in four cities showed no difference in contraceptive sales or appointments at medical facilities when these supplies and services were advertised in the regular mass media (Udry, 1972). Goldsmith (n.d.), however, says announcements on rock music stations are an effective method of reaching teen-agers.

Romantic love is a theme that pervades the movies (Knox, 1970), but while many of these movies show graphic scenes of sexual activity, rarely do they include any reference to contraception. One exception to this is the movie *Goodbye, Columbus,* in which the girl discontinues oral contraceptives but continues to have sexual intercourse for some time before acquiring a diaphragm.

Peers as a Resource

That leaves friends. The major source of information and help in progressing to the next stages of the prescription process comes from peers—girlfriends, boyfriends, and, occasionally, sisters. According to Goldsmith (n.d.), the most effective way of reaching teen-agers is through teen-agers who have already had experience with contraceptives. In England, Wadsworth, et al. (1971) report that "the commonest way of 'getting to know of the existence of the clinic' was reported as being from a friend." Information about methods is transmitted by word of mouth.

> The first time I had sex I didn't use anything. The second time I used rhythm—found out about it from my girlfriend.

Or:

> I heard about it [withdrawal] from a friend. I

thought it was best. I didn't know about any other methods. I didn't know about rhythm. My boyfriend knew about it. We discussed it before we had sex.

The ordinary way to find out about condoms and withdrawal is from a boyfriend. This can be either by word or, more directly, when the boyfriend uses a "rubber." Knowledge of other methods can come from the boy as well. One girl said, "The guy told me about foam."

This use of peers as a resource in preventing pregnancy is the basis of the next stage of the prescription process—the peer prescription stage.

CHAPTER III

The Peer Prescription Stage

EXPERIMENTING

In the peer prescription stage young people try to learn how to prevent pregnancy by discussing the problem with their peers. There is a great deal of experimentation involving a variety of birth control methods, variations in the use of the methods, variation in the number of methods used, and variations in the patterns of use.

Variety of Methods

The birth control methods most commonly used in this stage are rhythm, withdrawal (*coitus interruptus*), foam, condoms, and douche. Some young people experiment with materials that are not generally considered to be contraceptives, such as vaseline, plastic wrap used in place of condoms, and cola drinks, shaken and foaming, used as douches. One young woman believed that pregnancy could be avoided by drinking lots of water and urinating immediately after sex. Another was told by her mother to buy capsules in the drug store, empty them, replace the contents with baking soda, and insert one into the vagina before intercourse. The capsule, according to the mother, would be melted by the ejaculated semen during intercourse, freeing the baking soda to kill the sperm. For the most part, however, experimenting in this stage takes place with the first five methods mentioned above.

Birth control methods used in this stage are not confined

to contraceptives. They may be abortifacient also. A young laboratory assistant aborted herself with a catheter she obtained from the laboratory she worked in. Although she thought she was using sterile technique, she suffered a septic infection.

Variation in the Number of Methods Used

There is a great deal of variation in the number of methods used in the peer prescription stage. Generally, the longer a girl is in this stage the more methods she will use. (The exception to this is long-term use, described below.) An individual may use anywhere from one to five methods in this stage. Some examples of numbers of methods used and sequence of use appear in Chapter V, Patterns of Movement. A single method may not be used extensively, but it will be tried at least once.

Variation in the Use of Methods

A variation of withdrawal is partial penetration of the penis in the vagina. There are three variations on the rhythm method: avoiding intercourse during what the girls interviewed called "the middle" of the menstrual cycle; having intercourse only immediately before or after the menstrual period; and having intercourse during the menstrual period only. A girl who came to the clinic with a college math book tucked under her arm said she "only balled" during her period. These peer prescription variations on the rhythm method would seem to minimize the risk of conception to some extent since that risk is small in the early part of the menstrual cycle. It increases five days before the onset of ovulation and decreases after ovulation (Barrett and Marshall, 1969). The problem is determining when ovulation takes place.

Patterns of Use

There are many patterns of use. Methods can be used singly, that is, one at a time, or in combination. Single use can be long-term or shifting. In long-term use one method is selected and used steadily over a long period. One young woman used withdrawal for six and a half years. She then switched to the pill, on the advice of a physician, when her periods became irregular. Long-term use is more likely when there is a steady ongoing relationship with predictable sexual intercourse. One pregnant 24-year-old girl said:

> I come from a strict Catholic background where even thinking of sex outside of marriage was almost impossible. Unfortunately, I met a boy whom I felt I would marry and we decided to practice rhythm. We did so for four years until I got pregnant last month. [After having an abortion] I plan to use a proper method of prevention. I will go to the gynecologist I have just found and have him instruct me as to what method and procedure to follow.

Shifting, or changing from one method to another, can be either sequential or alternative. In sequential shifting each method is used for a time and is then followed by another method. An example is provided by a 23-year-old girl who first had intercourse when she was 13. The first method she had any experience with was the condom, which her boyfriend provided. She discontinued this method because, she said, it was "uncomfortable, probably psychological." Then she read about foam in a magazine and bought some at the drugstore. She used it for a year before discontinuing it because it was messy and her boyfriend didn't like it. In all, she used the condom, foam, rhythm, withdrawal, and douche before getting pills.

In alternative shifting, two or three methods are used by the couple, but only one is used at each intercourse. For example, within a short period of time, foam, withdrawal, and douche may all be used by a couple, a different method at each intercourse. Or a couple using rhythm may use condoms during the "unsafe" period of the menstrual cycle. A couple may use both patterns of shifting, that is, they may use single methods sequentially for a time and then use them alternately, or vice versa. One couple used withdrawal at the first coitus and then, after hearing about rhythm, shifted to that for a while. Later they alternated between rhythm and withdrawal, using rhythm when the girl was at her "safe" period and withdrawal at other times of the month.

When methods are combined, more than one method is used at each coitus. A very common combination is rhythm and withdrawal. Another is rhythm and foam. One couple went to the extreme of using four methods—condom, withdrawal, rhythm, and douche—all at the same time! Two methods can be used together regularly with a third used occasionally. A couple used a pattern of this type for four years, combining rhythm and withdrawal with the occasional use of condoms.

There are virtually as many patterns of use as there are combinations and permutations of the five methods used in the peer prescription stage. One of the reasons for frequent shifting is that sexual activity at this stage is still often intermittent and unpredictable. Another is the continual experimentation with methods of avoiding pregnancy, methods that the users themselves may devise or that they learn about from their peers.

PLANNED OR SPONTANEOUS USE

Birth control methods in the peer prescription stage may be used either spontaneously or with planning. Planned use of rhythm was illustrated above by the 24-year-old girl who eventually got pregnant and the girl who only had intercourse during her menstrual period. The rhythm method is spontaneous when a girl who is having intercourse "just happens" to be at a point in her menstrual cycle where she feels it is safe to do without a contraceptive.

Withdrawal is always available, so it lends itself to spontaneous use, but it is also used in a planned way, as was shown in the examples on long-term use.

Condoms and foam require some prior planning since they have to be purchased in advance, but once they are in the possession of the user there can be an element of spontaneity in their use. That girls are reluctant to prepare in this way has already been discussed. Condoms are most commonly supplied by the boy and used with no prior planning by the girl at all. In this case, there is birth control planning on the part of one partner but complete spontaneity on the part of the other.

Douching requires some prior planning since the equipment has to be available, but if coitus takes place spontaneously where it is located, it, too, can be used without prior planning.

PROBLEMS IN THE PEER PRESCRIPTION STAGE

Lack of Skills and Information

A major problem in the peer prescription stage is that boys and girls lack the skills and information they need if they are to avoid the pitfalls of the birth control methods they use. If condoms are put on improperly they can slip off and remain in the vagina when the male withdraws his penis after intercourse. They can break when the user has failed to leave some slack at the end to accommodate the ejaculated semen. In either case, the protection afforded by the condom is nullified.

Many girls who use foam are chagrined to discover that it has a very short span of effectiveness. They are upset when they learn that it must not only be inserted a very short time before sexual intercourse, but also each and every time coitus takes place during a single episode of sexual activity. A young woman who got pregnant while using foam said, "Too much time elapsed from time of application to time of ejaculation." Another girl said:

I bought foam. I heard about it from my girlfriend.

But I got scared of it—the applicator—and didn't
really know how to use it, so I put it away.

A third said:

I heard of withdrawal, but didn't exactly know what
it was. I just knew about it. I asked the boy to
withdraw and he said he would, but I realized later
that he didn't.

Characteristics of Boy-Girl Relationships

Difficulties in the boy-girl relationship that were discussed
in the previous chapter presage problems in the peer stage.
Changes in the nature of relationships necessitate readjustments.
This happens in serial relationships when a girl is involved with
someone for a while and then becomes involved with someone
else. One young woman would only have coitus immediately
after her menstrual period. She was able to do this consistently
for about five years because the boy she was going with was
"very considerate." Now that she is no longer going with him,
she finds that "some of the guys aren't that considerate," and
she has to get another birth control method.

A girl must depend on the male to withdraw. This is
hazardous if one is not sure of one's sexual partner. As one girl
put it, "Different boys have different habits."

Although the condom can be purchased by the girl, its use
depends on the boy. Since, however, it is traditionally supplied
by the male, girls are usually more reluctant to prepare with this
method than with any of the others.

Sex Patterns

Spontaneity and naturalness are disturbed by peer prescription methods. The natural flow of the sex act is interrupted.
A young woman whose boyfriend was using condoms said:

I don't want it. I feel self-conscious or uncomfortable. I feel it isn't right for him to use it. It's an imposition.

Another dimension of sexual activity that affects the use of peer prescription methods is the type of sexual activity involved. Methods that make use of creams, foams, or jellies are of concern to those who practice oral sex.

These problems that peer prescription methods present foster inconsistent and haphazard use: a method is used "most of the time;" or coitus takes place despite the fact that "we just didn't happen to have a condom with us that night;" or "we always used the rhythm method, but that time we got carried away;" or "he didn't pull out that time." A girl who had used contraceptive cream for four months acknowledged this effect when she said, "I only used it off and on because I didn't like it, so I didn't use it the way I should."

Many of these problems are minimized with increasing awareness, changes in self-concept, and greater comfort with the sex role. New attitudes develop toward even the most awkward and difficult methods, and techniques evolve to facilitate their use. One girl reported that her boyfriend inserts the applicator with the foam so that the procedure becomes part of the sexual foreplay. Another said, "It's in your head. When you feel easy with sex, and that's what you want to do, the method is secondary."

WHY PEER PRESCRIPTION?

The peer prescription stage is subject to many of the influences that exist in the natural stage. Patterns of sexual behavior, including frequency and predictability of sexual intercourse, continue to condition birth control behavior, as does belief in the effectiveness of the methods being used and the lack of a real commitment to nonmarital sex. The problem of whether one can dare to disclose one's sexual activity to a parent or to an expert in order to obtain help is of major importance in this stage.

Patterns of Sexual Behavior

The frequency of sexual intercourse continues to influence birth control behavior in the peer prescription stage. A girl chose rhythm because:

> There is nothing I want to take. I don't want to take pills, but if I start having sex frequently, like once a week, I will get pills. Until then I will use rhythm.

Belief in Effectiveness of Methods Used

Peer prescription methods are used in the belief that they are effective:

> My boyfriend said he thought it [withdrawal] would work. It made sense. If the sperm is not inside you, you can't get pregnant.

Or douching "will get everything out" and therefore prevent pregnancy. Withdrawal was used by one couple because:

> We thought it would work. Then we read something in a booklet given to us by my roommate that caused a scare, so we got a condom. We knew we needed something, so we tried it to see what it was like.

They used the condom once and then, while she waited for her appointment at a family planning clinic three months hence, she used birth control pills obtained from a friend.

Commitment to Sex

The methods used in this stage are compatible with the lack of a real commitment to sex. One girl, who was not sexually active at the time of data collection, had used withdrawal for six months before she broke up with her boyfriend. She said:

> I won't have sex now unless I like somebody a lot. I would wait three months before having sex. I would use withdrawal again. I won't use the pill or coil until I get married. I would like to wait till I'm married to have a lot of sex. If I do have it [coitus] once or twice before, I would use withdrawal again. If I find somebody I love a lot, I would use the coil.

Disclosure of Sexual Activity

At the peer prescription stage there is some readiness to acknowledge, to oneself and to one's partner, a commitment to sexual activity. This is in contrast to the natural stage, when the absence of such acknowledgment prevents awareness and discussion with the partner. The problem at this stage is that, while sexually active young people are aware of their need for a birth control method, they fear to disclose their sexual activity to parents and professionals. Those in the peer prescription stage avoid this problem by using methods that are learned from peers and that require no contact at all with anyone outside the peer group, or only the fleeting and impersonal contact of making a purchase at the drug store.

Rhythm and withdrawal are particularly suitable since they provide no material evidence whatever of sexual activity. A girl who had been using the rhythm method for a number of years came to a free clinic for an expert method when she moved away from her parents' home. She said she had been afraid to keep a contraceptive at home because her parents might have found it. "After all," she said, "it's a Catholic home and you're not supposed to do those things." Another girl hid her contraceptive under the mattress and lived in constant fear that her mother would find it. Besides fearing the family will find out about their sexual activity by discovering their contraceptives, many girls are afraid their parents will discover it indirectly through a doctor or other professional. A girl who found out through a friend that parental consent was not needed at a free clinic said:

> I came to the free clinic because it is the only place I can turn to. I couldn't go to my own doctor. He is too close to my family. It would kill my parents if they knew.

Disclosure directly to an expert is also difficult: "It [foam] was the only thing I knew about besides the pill, and I didn't want to go to a doctor."

Some of the reasons for the difficulty girls have in disclosing sexual activity directly to professionals is discussed in the chapter on the expert stage (Chapter IV).

Other forms of disclosure that are feared are reflected in questions girls ask about whether oral contraceptives can be detected through blood tests or whether medical histories require information about medications that are being taken.

Thus, the peer prescription stage, with its flexibility and its many patterns of use, provides the psychological conditioning necessary for change, for making the transitions from little awareness to greater awareness, from noncommitment to commitment, from one self-concept to another, and, finally, from no birth control use to planned birth control use. It evolves into the next stage—the expert stage.

CHAPTER IV

The Expert Stage

The changes that take place in a girl in the natural and peer stages culminate in a readiness to disclose her sexual activity to an expert in order to obtain an effective means of avoiding pregnancy. An "expert" is anyone whose knowledge, by virtue of education and profession, is above that of the peer. This includes doctors, nurses, and paraprofessionals who have the legal and social mandate to dispense birth control methods. Girls in the expert stage have to face the problems of making and maintaining contact with an expert and continuing the use of an expert prescription.

> I was shy about it when I was younger. I'm bolder about it now. I'm having sex and you have to recognize that.

And:

> I couldn't go to a family planning clinic a couple of years ago, but now I'm more aggressive about it. I insist on my right to have birth control now.

Initiating the use of an expert method of birth control does not guarantee continued use. A method that has been acquired and used for some time may be discontinued despite all the ambivalence, fear, doubt, and difficulty with self, boyfriends, parents, and experts that have gone into the decision to acquire it.

CHANGES IN SEXUAL PATTERNS

A change in the frequency of coitus is a prime mover throughout the prescription process. The direction of the movement, whether it be toward progress or retrogression, depends on the direction of this change. Thus, changing patterns of sexual activity are as important to movement in the process at this stage as in the natural stage.

The most usual reason for moving from the peer prescription stage to the expert stage is an increase in the frequency of coitus. For example, one young woman only had coitus about 12 times in her first four sexually active years. Then she got the pill because she was "making it more. Now that I am having sex more often, I need a more effective method."

Decrease in the frequency of coitus is one of the major reasons for discontinuing an expert birth control method and reverting to the peer or natural stage. Just as girls do not start taking the pill unless there are immediate and concrete prospects of having regular sexual intercourse, so they do not like to continue taking it when they feel there is little likelihood of coitus. After breaking off a relationship a girl said, "I'm not going with anyone in particular so I don't have a need for pills." Another young woman said:

> I took pills for three years. I quit about five months ago because I hadn't had intercourse for such a long time. It seemed a waste of money and time. Then about two months ago I met a guy who told me he had his cords tied and couldn't get me pregnant. Apparently he lied, and I'm now one and a half months pregnant.

A change in sex patterns due to marriage has the same effect as a change in sex patterns in nonmarital situations. A girl who is married perceives an increase in the frequency of coitus as one cause for obtaining an expert prescription just as does the girl who is not married. The difference is that marriage makes it easier to disclose sexual activity to the expert.

Likewise, the effects of a decrease in the frequency of coitus are not unique to unmarried women. The girl whose sexual patterns change due to separation or divorce from her husband retrogresses like the one who breaks up with a boyfriend:

> Due to separation from my husband, I was not having relations with anyone. Then my husband and I unexpectedly got together and that was it! I thought my period was due, and therefore didn't take any precautions.

One young woman was advised by her physician to discontinue the oral contraceptive she had been using for two years. He did not volunteer to recommend an alternative method and she did not ask for one because she was separated from her husband and saw no need. In circumstances like this, if a reunion with a husband or boyfriend unexpectedly takes place, the couple may have intercourse without using a contraceptive.

Another young woman had difficulties both with oral contraceptives and an intrauterine device during her marriage. She shifted to the diaphragm, which she used as long as she remained in a stable marital situation. After separating from her husband, however, the only method she ever used was rhythm—she planned to get an abortion if she became pregnant.

Since changing patterns of sexual activity can cause movement in the prescription process to go in either direction—toward progression or toward retrogression—the problem of avoiding pregnancy continues even after entry into the expert stage.

MAKING CONTACT WITH THE EXPERT

Finding Out Where to Go

Finding out how to gain access to an expert and where to go for birth control services is a major problem for young unmarried women. "I was embarrassed and didn't know how to go about finding a doctor." The usual way for a young person to get expert help, particularly medical help, is through her parents, but as we have seen in a previous chapter, parents are not a resource for help with birth control.

Even girls who know about birth control methods usually do not know how to get them. Two high school science majors used luck and rhythm, the latter "because it lowered the chances of getting pregnant." One had done this for two and a half years, the other for ten months. They thought they had to be 18 to get pills at a clinic. When they heard from a friend that this was not true, they came to the clinic because it was the only place they knew where they could get help about birth control.

One very common way of finding out about birth control and where to get it is to get pregnant:

> I didn't know I could come here [to the free clinic] and get pills. I didn't want to ask my mom. I didn't know anywhere else where I could get it. When I was pregnant I had to go to counseling. A social worker told me a number of places. The free clinic was closest.

A pregnancy scare can have the same effect. A girl, who came to a public health clinic for a pregnancy test which proved negative, had the following exchange with a birth control counselor during an information rap session:

Girl. Where can I get it [foam]?
Counselor. Here.
Girl. Can I get it tonight?
Counselor. Yes.
Girl. Oh! I want it, I want it.
Counselor. It is not as effective as the pills.
Girl. Can I get them here? Can I get them tonight? I want them. I want them!

One young woman selected a gynecologist from the yellow pages of a phone book, but this is not usual. The major source of information about where to go for birth control services is, again, friends:

My sister and her girlfriend came to the free clinic and told me about it.

Or:

I chose Planned Parenthood because a girl I knew used it—that was in Berkeley. I came to the free clinic when I got to Los Angeles—I found out about it from friends.

Or friends may call attention to an advertisement:

We were wondering how we could get pills before we knew about the free clinic. We thought she would go to a doctor and say we were planning to get married. I was thinking that we would go together to my Kaiser insurance. I didn't know if it would work, but it was worth a try. But then a friend showed us an article in the *Free Press* about the free clinic.

Constraints in Making Contact

Even when a girl knows where to go there are constraints in making contact. These constraints take place on two levels. One is on an impersonal level that has to do with the organization of the delivery of birth control services and the social and legal restrictions that govern it. The other is on a personal level and grows out of the face-to-face situation between the girl and the expert.

Impersonal constraints include age, marital status, finances, transportation, the way services are organized, and the attitudes of professionals.

Rules governing age and marital status in this area are unclear—"You wonder how old you have to be." Girls hesitate to seek services for fear they will be refused on the basis of age or marital status. This is particularly true of girls under 18. A 16-year-old who came to a free clinic for a pregnancy test said, "I didn't get a birth control method before because I didn't know a 16-year-old could get it." Another "just found out through a friend that you don't need your parents' consent." But even older girls who are not married may worry about whether they can get birth control services. A 20-year-old who was pregnant and planning to get an abortion had been using withdrawal at the time of conception. She had not acquired an expert method because, as she said, "I didn't know the pill was as easy to get as it is and I was too chicken to go get it."

A young woman who had her mother's consent reported:

> The doctor I had was really screwed. I didn't like him. He seemed cold. He was an old man. He was really prejudiced toward me. He said, "You're not married?" I said, "No." He said, "Well, are you sure? Does your mother know?" My mother was with me.

This example illustrates how impersonal constraints influence interaction on the personal level.

The common euphemisms for birth prevention and birth control bolster the belief that marriage is a necessary requirement for obtaining services. Davis (1967) says that it is well known that "family planning" is a euphemism for contraception. Kantner and Zelnik (1969) report that this "professional" or "euphemistic" term is not familiar to black women as it relates to fertility. That family planning is felt to be "for newlyweds, not for single people" and "the word 'parenthood' would put you off" is further illustrated by the following exerpt from a group interview:

> *Interviewer.* Do you think you could go to a family planning or Planned Parenthood Clinic?
>
> *First girl.* Family planning—they'd want you to be married.
>
> *Second girl.* Will they help you if you're not married?
>
> *Interviewer.* What's your guess?
>
> *Second girl.* It sounds like you'd have to be married.

If age or marital status are not requisites, evidence of sexual activity may be. A young woman who went to her family physician said:

> They'll give it to you if you're living with a man. At first the nurse snickered and said they couldn't help me. She was a witch. Then the doctor found out I was *living* with a man and said O.K.

It is of interest to note that a review of the legal restrictions on the delivery of birth control services to unmarried minors shows that the trend in legislation, as well as in the courts, has been overwhelmingly in the direction of facilitating the delivering of such services. "There appeared to have been no case in which a doctor or medical facility had been prosecuted criminally or sued for damages for having examined or treated a minor in connection with contraception with or without parental consent" (Pilpel and Wechsler, 1971).

Social restrictions are also lessening, as evidenced by the change in the policies of the major medical organizations in the United States such as Planned Parenthood/World Population, American Association of Planned Parenthood Physicians, the American Medical Association, the American College of Obstetricians and Gynecologists, the American Academy of Pediatrics, and the American Academy of Family Physicians (Pilpel and Wechsler, 1969, 1971).

Lack of money inhibits contact with the expert. Not only are financial resources limited in this age group, but most girls have no experience on which to base an estimate of the possible cost of services. If you "didn't know the clinic gave away free pills" you would do without or resort to something else. A young woman who was using foam chose it because it was reasonably priced and did not require a prescription. She said, "If I had to get a prescription I would have to go to a doctor and I don't have any money." There is concern about choice of methods in relation to finances as well as whether a method can be had at all:

> I have a terrible memory and hate to take pills, but I heard that they don't give IUD's or diaphragms here and I don't have any money, so am I stuck with pills?

Transportation can be yet another hindrance. Public transportation may not be available at all. If it is, it may be inefficient, requiring a great deal of time and effort to use. A long bus ride may end in arriving at a clinic too late for the hours that have been stipulated for birth control services.

Private transportation may not be readily available. Young women do not usually own their own cars, and access to the family car, if there is one, may be limited. Many parents require an accounting of where the car is being driven and for what purpose before they will allow it to be used by a junior member of the family. If a girl can get the family car for a limited time only, she may not be able to drive to the source of service, wait the time necessary, and get the car back in the time allotted to her. Arrangements to accommodate the time problems raised by transportation, clinic hours, and school or work hours are made more difficult by the inability to disclose one's sexual activity to parents.

A young woman at a public health youth clinic had to get the family car back at a stipulated time. She had already seen the doctor and he had prescribed an oral contraceptive, but the final requirement before the pills were actually dispensed was that she attend the information session that was conducted by the public health nurse. She had driven from another county where there were no birth control services for young women and had just enough time to return the car to the family. It was suggested that she call home and advise her parents that she would be late. This she did with some trepidation.

Aside from transportation problems, there are problems concerning the organization of professional services for those in the expert stage. In clinics that provide young women with the services of volunteer physicians, the delivery of services may at times be haphazard. When a young woman was informed that she could not get her prescription renewed because the doctor would not be present that evening, she said:

> But, man, I'm taking off from work. The clinic is open exactly when I work. I'll have to take off from work again and risk my job to come here.

On the other hand, the doctor may be present but is unavailable for other reasons. A young woman, in this case married, arrived at a large metropolitan hospital where she had previously received a three-month supply of oral contraceptives. She had taken time from work and driven a considerable distance. She said she had been told to come back when she ran out of pills, but she had not been told she had to have an appointment. She had tried to call but, as she said, "Have you ever tried to call this place and get through to the right person?" When she was refused service, she said,

> I didn't use anything before and I didn't get pregnant, so O.K. I won't use anything again. Besides, I'm married now and if I get pregnant it wouldn't be so terrible.

Another problem in the interaction between young women and family planning experts is handling the anger of parents who discover their daughters' contraceptives. One mode of handling this problem came to light at a conference of professionals and paraprofessionals in the family planning field to which a panel of young people was invited to discuss teen-age birth control problems. The discussion began when some of the professionals expressed concern about telephone calls they had recived from irate parents. The professionals felt the young women should do their part and be more discreet in handling their birth control materials. In other words, hide them, don't let your parents find them. The young women took this opportunity to ask for help in changing their parents' attitudes about sex and birth control. They felt their parents were not cognizant of their needs and of the realities of the situation. They were not "looking at their kids and seeing where they were at." They cited many instances where their attempts to talk to their parents were disregarded and they asked for help from the adult professionals in communicating their needs to their parents. Although the professionals expressed no unanimous point of view, a vocal portion felt that their responsibility ended with the provision of contraceptives and that it was the responsibility of the young women to inform their parents of their activities and try to make them understand their point of view, and that failure to do so was an indication of the young women's lack of responsibility about sex relations and birth control.

Another mode of handling this question is when the professional is confronted with an irate parent and considers it to be part of his or her job to handle the confrontation. In this situation the professional is willing to share with the young woman the responsibility of communicating with the parent.

In both of these modes of handling parental anger the professionals are aware that they are providing services without the knowledge and consent of parents, but in the first case they want to be left out of any involvement with parents and in the second case they are willing to get involved with them.

These two different ways of handling this question have an effect on the birth control behavior of young women. While in both cases birth control services are being made available, where the professional does not want to get involved it encourages a young woman to be clandestine despite her desire to be open and despite her request for help in being open. This reinforces her own ambivalence and lack of commitment to sex. It also retards the growth of a new self-concept by impeding the social acceptance necessary for the change in self-concept.

All of this raises questions about the role of professional and paraprofessional family planners who are involved with young unmarried women. Should they merely deliver services or should they also be prepared to be involved in educating and counselling with their young clients? Further, should they also be prepared to be involved in educating and counselling the parents?

Underlying the different modes of delivering birth control services and the different modes of handling parental anger is the variety of attitudes toward premarital sex among family planning workers that is similar to the variety of attitudes among parents discussed in an earlier chapter. Some want to restrict all premarital sexual activity, some want to restrict only certain types of sexual activity, some recognize that premarital sex cannot be restricted but do not wholeheartedly approve of it, and some approve of it. For some, it is all right to have sex relations "with someone you love" if you're not married, but "just to go to parties and have relations with anyone there" is not.

Personal constraints grow out of the face-to-face situation between a girl and an expert. The first thing the girl must do is initiate contact by presenting herself for professional services. This is only the beginning of successful birth control use, for she must continue to see the expert for checkups, monitoring, and the resolution of any problems that arise in the course of using an expert method.

Aversion to the expert makes initial contact difficult for the girl. Aversion has two components: (1) the girl's feeling of social distance from the expert, which makes her afraid to trust and confide in a stranger, and (2) psychological pain, which involves modesty and the memory of disagreeable experiences. Some girls are less fearful with a woman expert, but this seems to be less important than the other factors just mentioned. The following excerpt from a birth control rap session illustrates the social distance and psychological pain that lead to aversion difficulties in the relationship with the expert:

> *First girl.* We went steady for two years and discussed birth control but didn't do anything about it.
>
> *Counselor.* Why didn't you get birth control? What was it that stopped you from coming for birth control before this?
>
> *First girl.* I was scared to come.

Counselor.   Why?

First girl.   Because of doctors.

Counselor.   What do you mean by that? What is it about doctors that makes you feel that way?

Second girl.   I hate doctors.

Counselor.   Why?

Second girl.   Because of modesty. I'm modest. I'm uncomfortable when I go in and have an exam. I know a lot of girls who are modest and don't want to be examined by a man they don't know. Doctors look at it from a medical point of view, but girls don't.

Counselor.   Would you feel better with a woman doctor?

Second girl.   Yes.

First girl.   I don't think it's that. It's that doctors are so professional.

Counselor.   How does that affect going to them?

First girl.   You can't trust them. You can't really tell them what's wrong.

A boy.   It's like going to Big Daddy with your tail between your legs. It's really the establishment. It seems like you always have someone to confide in, a friend or something like that, but the doctor is a stranger. Also, it might get back.

Counselor.   Get back where?

Boy.   Might get back to your friends or parents.

Sometimes previous experiences with an insensitive expert contributes to building up aversion in girls. As a 19-year-old girl said:

I don't like doctors. I get nervous when I have to go. All they ever meant to me was hurt. Many are sarcastic and make wise remarks about my weight.

> When I had a pelvic examination one said, "If you get any bigger I'll have to take a miner's lamp down there."

The pelvic examination becomes a focus for aversion. It is an unknown. Many girls have never heard of it, and those who have often do not understand its purpose or realize that it is a requirement for expert birth control prescription. Others avoid the pelvic examination despite their knowledge:

> The idea of an internal exam scares me. I would have gotten the pill long ago if not for that. I haven't had one yet.

Since the girls have been through a considerable period of struggle with their ambivalence and fears of disclosure before deciding to acquire a birth control method, the pelvic exam is, so to speak, a moment of truth, and may result in some unanticipated behavior in the examining room. Some girls cry. One girl jumped off the table and refused to continue with the examination. Even when there is no overt behavior of this kind, the pelvic examination is an event fraught with anxiety. Professionals or experts, on the other hand, often expect that once a girl has exposed herself sexually she should feel no compunction about allowing herself to be examined. They may become impatient and, not realizing the source of the distress, may, as one doctor put it, "feel like slapping her and sending her out of the examining room." Although they refrain from such behavior, their feelings may prevent them from handling the situation with the delicacy and sensitivity that is needed. This may perpetuate the problem of aversion in the expert stage when continuous interaction with the expert is a necessity.

Negative reactions by some physicians toward girls who are seeking a birth control method may be due to personal religious and moral beliefs, hostility toward women, ambivalent feelings about sex, or inadequate education in medical school. Some physicians, on the other hand, are so motivated by a sense of the importance of birth control that they tend to be overenthusiastic and even dictatorial in urging a method on a patient, so much so that it constitutes an intrusion on privacy (Wolf and Ferguson, 1969). Unfortunately, the emphasis in medical school courses on birth control is on the biological rather than the behavioral components, and few faculty members are ready or willing to offer as much instruction in the latter as medical students desire (Coombs, 1968).

A young woman who received a three-month supply of pills at her first examination did not return to renew her supply because she was so disturbed by the events surrounding the pelvic examination:

> I was afraid to come back because of my experience before. The doctor was cold. I had a pelvic and didn't know about it or what was happening. I hadn't been expecting it and didn't know what it was all about.

In the words of a black, high school educated, paraprofessional birth control expert who has had considerable personal and professional experience with poor and pregnant teen-agers, "You have to treat these girls like delicate flowers" in order to perpetuate the continuous interaction with them that is necessary for successful birth control use. Like most paraprofessionals in this field, this woman instinctively understood the problems these girls have far better than do many of the middle-class physicians attending them, which is precisely why paraprofessionals are being used in clinics.

Many of the new clinics are developing methods that minimize the chances of aversion interfering with the continuing use of an expert birth control method. For a description of an initial visit to one of these clinics, see Goldsmith (1969).

The impact of impersonal constraints having to do with age and marital and financial status are dispelled more easily than constraints on the personal level, which continue to influence the relationship between the girl and the expert throughout the expert stage. Aversion may never be completely overcome, but experience makes it possible to deal with the situation:

> It doesn't bother me to go to a doctor now. Not like it did when I was younger. I was shy then and it made me nervous.

RISKS VERSUS BENEFITS OF METHODS

As part of her decision to go to an expert, a girl will weigh the risks of the expert methods that are available against their benefits. Although condoms, foam, and rhythm may be used in the expert stage, generally when a girl consults an expert she is aware that oral contraceptives, intrauterine devices, and diaphrams are the methods most likely to be recommended.

Oral Contraceptives

The anticipated risks involved in taking oral contraceptives are of two types—specific and unspecific. *Specific anticipation* occurs when a girl presents problems, or has a family history of problems, that contraindicate the use of an oral contraceptive. Diabetes, kidney disease, blood clotting, high blood pressure, varicose veins, and adverse reactions to some other medications are a few examples of such problems. A girl may be informed by a physician of the inadvisability of her using a specific method; she may read about expert opinions in newspapers or magazines; or she may have heard about risks from friends or family. In many cases, what she hears or reads actually could contraindicate the use of oral contraceptives. An example of specifically anticipating adverse effects from oral contraceptives is provided by a young woman who said:

> I wouldn't like the pill. I have a weird system and wouldn't be able to use the pill. The coil is less of a hassle. I react strangely to a lot of medication, like penicillin. I'm allergic to a lot of things.

Specific anticipation sometimes occurs in young black women who fear that the blood disease, sickle cell anemia, which is more prevalent among blacks than among whites, may make them especially susceptible to blood disorders (such as clotting) that have been attributed to the pill.

Unlike specific anticipation, which may be based on a specific problem, *unspecific anticipation* is something that has been "heard about," usually through newspapers, magazines, and word of mouth. It includes worrying about such things as blood clots, death, cancer, bad effects in general, adverse effects on body metabolism, multiple births, possible ill effects from starting to use the pill at an early age, possible ill effects from prolonged use, birth anomalies, female complications, sterility, and effects on specific organs which may be expressed in terms like, "It eats your liver."

Anticipation and concern over the effects of oral contraceptives are manifested in the questions young women ask about them, such as:

> I'm 17. I've never used any kind of birth control. Is birth control dangerous? Does your baby come out with a problem if you take the pill too long?

> I've used foam and pills. If I continue to use pills, how long should I take them, and does prolonged usage cause female complications?

I'm 18. I've used birth control pills for three years. I'm definitely uptight about them. I wonder if it wasn't perhaps harmful to start taking them so young. I also wonder how important it is to get regular checkups.

What are the advantages and disadvantages? What are the side effects and the chances of getting them? Can you stop them at any time with no harm done? Do you need an examination before you are given the pills?

Can you die from the pill?

Is there real danger of breast cancer with the pills?

Are there any bad effects caused from the pill? Can it in any way cause multiple births?

Occasionally a young girl who has never had sexual intercourse will have had a negative experience with oral contraceptives that she has been advised to use for medical reasons. Such was the case with one young woman, who was unaware of the nature of the medication she was taking:

I was on the pill for an ovarian cyst before I had sex, when I was in high school, being chasted [*sic*]. No one told me it was *the* pill. They made me sick. I vomited. So I quit taking them. Every morning I'd drop it down the toilet. Then I had sex and then I got the pill again. I got sick. I changed pills. I took them for five months, then I went off for a month and then started again. I am taking pills now.

The beneficial aspects of oral contraception are that (1) it is an effective birth control method, (2) it is easy and convenient to use, and (3) it allows for simulation of natural sexual intercourse. Since most young women have had experience with other kinds of pills, they do not need to learn new skills and techniques. They don't have to do anything they haven't done before.

> It's the safest. Others are a big hassle. Why do all that stuff when you can just pop a pill, like vitamins?

Hearing about the experiences of others may affect—favorably as well as adversely—how a girl will feel about using the pill. Fear of the pill can be overcome by knowing others who are using it successfully and without detrimental effects.

Forgetting to take pills daily may be a problem, and the common advice of doctors to "put it by your toothbrush so you won't forget" is not possible for young women who have to hide their pills from their parents so as not to disclose their sexual activity.

Intrauterine Devices

An intrauterine device is a possible birth control solution, but young women are aware that there are special problems related to its use by girls who have never been pregnant. Indeed, the risk of expulsion declines sharply with age, and the risk of removal for bleeding or pain is highest among women with few or no children (Tietze, 1970). Questions about the IUD are common:

> Will a doctor insert an IUD in an unmarried girl? Are there any dangers in this? I have heard only women who have had children can use IUDs—true?

There is some hesitancy about having something "put inside

you that you weren't born with." There is also concern about pain when the device is inserted, subsequent cramping, and alteration of menstrual flow. On the other hand, it is very appealing to some young women because it is a one-shot treatment that requires a minimum of attention and effort after it is inserted. This is especially important to girls who feel they would forget to take a pill every day. They like the idea of an intrauterine device because "You don't have to worry. You don't have to hassle with the pill, taking it everyday. You have peace of mind."

Diaphragm

The diaphragm is not a popular method. It is believed to be messy and inconvenient, and to take away from spontaneity and naturalness. Also, it is difficult to carry at all times, and it provides material evidence of sexual activity. Unlike the pill, it requires new skills and techniques. The following quote illustrates some of these problems:

> It was uncomfortable. I tried two different sizes and it was still uncomfortable. I don't think it fits properly. Besides, it was a hassle to use. I'd forget to put it in and have to stop and put it in. I had difficulty putting it in. It would slip out of my hands. And then I was always afraid it wasn't in right.

When the diaphragm is chosen, the choice is related to the predictability and frequency of coitus, and to anticipated risks of oral contraceptives:

> I didn't want the pill because I heard about blood clots and weight gain. I figured that if I needed it every other night it might be worth it [taking the pill], but with the number of times I need it in a

month [about three or four times] it isn't worth taking any risks. The diaphragm is convenient for me. I know in advance when I'm going to have sex relations. I would probably take the pill if I were living with a man.

In that it requires deliberate thought and planning, the diaphragm has some similarity to some of the methods that are used in the peer prescription stage and, like those, will be used more readily by girls who feel somewhat secure in their new self-concept. It is also used when some sexual restraints are desired since it requires a deliberate, conscious act at each coitus.

Abortion

Abortion is a universal phenomenon. It is still the most widespread, and the most clandestine, method of fertility control in the world (Tietze and Lewitt, 1969). Wherever legal abortion has been permitted it has been widely practiced, and this is, in part, merely a shift from nonlegal and medically dangerous abortions to abortions with little risk (Stycos, 1964). As a birth control method abortion can be used as part of a plan for birth control or as an emergency measure. Its use as an emergency measure will be discussed in a later chapter.

As part of a plan for birth control, abortion may be used alone or in combination with another method. Its use alone is rare in this country due to the many moral, legal, medical, and social barriers that prevail. Despite these barriers, there is some indication that this may be the method of choice for a few young women. One girl, who had had an abortion when she was 15, was planning, at 17, to get another, since "another abortion doesn't sound like such a big deal."

Barriers against abortion operate to deter its use in combination with other methods, but such use is becoming a little more common. Using abortion in combination with other methods is referred to by professionals as a back-up method, to be used only in the event of a contraceptive method failure. But there are signs that some young women incline toward a more liberal interpretation. They consider abortion to be an acceptable form of birth control and plan to use it in combination with what they know is a less effective method. One young woman objected to the pill because of possible adverse effects, refused to use the diaphragm for esthetic reasons, and had difficulties with an intrauterine device. She planned to use the rhythm method and have an abortion if and when she became pregnant. Another young woman was obtaining information for her third abortion. Abortions in two different foreign countries had terminated her two previous pregnancies. Although abortion was technically illegal in both of those countries, they were not difficult to obtain. Her experience had led her to view abortion as a reasonable method of birth control. Her use of a contraceptive was fairly regular but not meticulous, and abortion was definitely part of her routine birth control plan in the event of pregnancy.

DISCONTINUING AN EXPERT METHOD

The risks and benefits of the various expert methods of birth control continue to be considered by young women after acquiring and using a method.

Anticipated or Experienced Adverse Effects

Anticipated or actually experienced adverse effects are a major reason for discontinuing an expert method of birth control. After taking oral contraceptives for some time, anticipated side effects may lead a girl to decide that she doesn't want to take them anymore. "I don't want to take anything that will mess up my metabolism." If she discontinues oral contraceptives because of experienced side effects, she may later decide to "try pills again, and then I might go on to something else," even though she may not "like the idea of an IUD or diaphragm."

One girl tried three kinds of pills. The first made her nauseous and the second "acted like a real upper [stimulant]" and made her "feel hopped up all the time." Although she seemed to be doing well on the third pill, she was uneasy about it and was thinking about getting an IUD, even though she was afraid because she heard they were painful.

If a girl who anticipates adverse side effects from her expert birth control method begins to have infrequent and unpredictable coitus, she may discontinue the method. The contraceptive may be worth the risk when sexual intercourse is regular and frequent, but not when sex is irregular:

> I didn't have a regular sexual relationship. I didn't anticipate having sexual intercourse that time [when conception occurred]. I would use the pill just in anticipation of intercourse.

Temporary or Permanent Discontinuance

A birth control method may be discontinued temporarily or permanently, depending on why it is discontinued. Temporary discontinuance is indicated for intermittent vaginal infestations. A 16-year-old girl, whose physician advised her to discontinue oral contraceptives temporarily in order to clear up a vaginal infection, said:

> I stopped taking pills to clear up an infection because the pills made it worse. I stopped for one month only and I got pregnant. We used a condom, but the condom broke and I got pregnant.

Permanent discontinuance is indicated for some types of medical complications:

> I have a thyroid condition and other female problems. Most pills mess up my system. My doctor suggested that I not use pills, but I will rather than get pregnant again. I hope to get an IUD and I will also try to find a pill I can use. My doctor didn't want to put in an IUD until he was sure my female problems were cleared up (I was in the hospital a month ago for a D and C). He said a diaphragm was about the same as using foam and a rubber. We used rhythm in addition to foam and a rubber, but I still got pregnant.

With or Without Expert Consultation

In addition to discontinuing expert birth control methods because of anticipated or experienced adverse side-effects, and discontinuing them temporarily or permanently, birth control methods in the expert stage may be discontinued with or without consulting an expert. The girls in the two examples given above discontinued *with* consultation. In both cases, the side-effects were experienced rather than anticipated. Those who discontinue *without* consultation may also have either anticipated or experienced side-effects. Here is an example of the first:

> I had been afraid of the harmful side-effects of the pill such as clots, varicose veins, weight gain, and others. I quit taking them. Then I was just relying on rhythm, which, of course, failed.

The following is an example of experiencing side-effects, in this case weight gain, and discontinuing the method without consultation:

I took the pill for four years. I gained a lot of weight.
(I lost 14 pounds when I discontinued the pill.) Also
got to thinking about hormone changes and what the
pill does to the body.

In this case, the combination of an anticipated side-effect and
an experienced side-effect (weight gain) caused the girl to
discontinue the oral contraceptive.

With or Without an Alternative Method

When a method is discontinued on the advice of an
physician, he may or may not recommend an alternative
method. Even when an alternative method is recommended,
there may be insufficient instruction in the techniques necessary for its proper use, or even no instruction at all. The
importance of teaching these techniques was shown by a
controlled study of poor adolescent girls who had already had
one pregnancy. The control group, which was given standard
planned pregnancy treatment, had three times as many repeat
pregnancies as the group that was given a specially designed
birth control program. The relative success of the latter group
was attributed, not to increased motivation, but to the fact that
the girls were carefully taught the techniques necessary for good
birth control (Furstenberg, 1969).

One young woman who was having trouble with the pill
was told by a doctor to stop taking it for a two-month period so
that he could check for normal menstruation. First he recommended foam as a substitute. When that posed too many
problems, he advised using condoms. The girl said:

I couldn't use it without getting infections. I asked to
be fitted with a diaphragm, but was advised to
continue with condoms. The condoms were getting
left in me for a few minutes. At that, I would douche

right after intercourse. Then I used a combination of
rhythm and douche and I got pregnant.

When the condoms presented difficulties due to the girl's
inexperience and lack of skill, she went on to use another
combination of methods on her own.

Experience in the prescription process may make it easier
to use an alternative method after discontinuing the pill. One
young woman had used rhythm, condoms, and withdrawal in
the peer prescription stage before adopting the pill in the expert
stage. When she discontinued the pill because it caused brown
spots to appear on her skin, she retrogressed to the peer
prescription stage and used foam regularly. In another case, a
girl who entered the expert stage directly from the natural stage
was advised by her doctor to discontinue the pill because of a
vaginal infection. He did not recommend an alternative method.
She retrogressed to the natural stage. Both of these young
women got pregnant. Although the more experienced girl acted
to lower her chances of pregnancy, the outcome was the same
for both. That retrogression is fairly common when an
alternative method is not prescribed is shown by a study,
conducted by a physician, which indicated that 14 out of 100
women became pregnant "due to a doctor's failure to provide
an alternative method of family planning satisfactory to the
patient" (Chang-Silva, et al., 1971).

Some girls plan to abstain from sex at least temporarily
after discontinuing the pill, but the resolve to abstain often
fails. After using the pill for four years a young woman was
advised by her physician to discontinue it for two months. She
thought she would abstain from sex, but "something came up.
We thought he would withdraw, but he didn't."

Difference of Opinion Among Experts

A girl who discontinues an expert method because of

adverse side-effects may be influenced by differences of opinion among experts. A young woman with tumors was given contradictory advice by two physicians; one advised her not to take the pill at all and another advised her to try them for two months. She followed the second advice and experienced several side-effects—tender breasts, lack of energy, weight gain, and stomachaches. Without further consultation she discontinued the pill and bought suppositories that were labelled "contraceptive." She used one "for the one and only time and got pregnant."

Married and Unmarried Women

Again, these problems are not unique to unmarried women. Married women also discontinue contraceptives because of adverse side-effects and retrogress in the prescription process. One young married woman said:

> After my baby was born a year and a half ago my hands and fingers went numb. I was under treatment by an internist for this. He thought it was due to a hormone deficiency and would not allow me to take oral contraceptives. Therefore, it was either strict rhythm method or not having the use of my hands. Which would you choose?

Another woman, who had two children that were born during her marriage, separated from her husband. She had been taking the pill for two years and was advised by her doctor to discontinue for six months. He did not recommend an alternative method and she did not ask for one because of the separation. Unexpected coitus resulted in a pregnancy.

Adverse effects may occur with the use of intrauterine devices as well as with oral contraceptives. Often young women expel the device, sometimes repeatedly. Or they may experience excessive discomfort or menstrual disturbances. Also, there is a great deal of divergence of opinion among experts with regard to the intrauterine device. Some are reluctant to consider it for women who have never borne children while others are opposed to it for any woman because they feel that the presence of a foreign body in the uterus for a protracted length of time is potentially harmful.

Two Kinds of Movement

The examples of discontinuing a birth control method that have been cited illustrate the two kinds of movement that take place in the expert stage of the prescription process. One is shifting from one expert-prescribed method to another. The new method may be as effective as the old, or, if it is less effective, it is used with techniques that bring it to its level of maximum effectiveness. This type of movement, which necessitates consultation with an expert, includes shifting from oral contraceptives to intrauterine devices or even to condoms or foam. The other kind of movement is retrogression to the natural stage or peer stage of the prescription process. This happens, obviously, when no consultation is sought. The examples given of girls who discontinued expert methods because of changes in their sexual patterns illustrate this, as do the examples of those who discontinued without expert consultation because of side effects. Retrogression also occurs with expert consultation when the expert does not recommend an alternative method, or when he neglects to describe the skills and techniques necessary for the most effective use of an alternative method. The examples cited illustrate that when this happens behavior resembles either natural stage behavior or peer stage experimental behavior.

This discussion on discontinuance and retrogression shows that entering the expert stage of the prescription process does not end the problem of preventing pregnancy. After a woman discontinues an expert method, she may become pregnant whether or not she continues to consult an expert. Pregnancy as a consequence of the birth control prescription process is discussed further in Chapter VI.

CHAPTER V

Patterns of Movement

When the individual careers of girls in the prescription process are traced by single methods, one finds virtually as many careers as there are individuals. The listing below illustrates this by showing the sequence of birth control methods used by 15 young women.

Individual	Sequence of Methods Used
1	nothing–withdrawal–condom
2	nothing–rhythm–condom–nothing
3	nothing–rhythm–condom–withdrawal + douche
4	nothing–rhythm–douche–condom–pill
5	nothing–rhythm–withdrawal–condom–douche–pill
6	nothing–rhythm–withdrawal–douche–pill
7	withdrawal–condom–diaphragm + rhythm
8	foam–pill
9	foam–pill–foam
10	rhythm–condom–pill
11	withdrawal–pill–condom
12	condom–pill–condom
13	condom–pill
14	rhythm–condom–foam–pill
15	condom–rhythm

When careers of individual girls are traced by stages in the prescription process, some definite patterns appear. In the chapters on the three stages it was shown that movement can take place in two directions—progressively (from using no contraceptive to using expert methods) and retrogressively (from using expert methods back to peer methods or no methods at all). These movements can take place in a linear fashion through each of the stages or by skipping one or more stages. The flow chart illustrates the positions of 102 never-pregnant girls in the prescription process at a given point in time, and shows the pathways they took to arrive at their present positions.

The most common pattern is entry into the prescription process at the stage of natural prescription, followed by movement in a linear fashion, without skipping stages, to the stage of peer prescription and then to the expert stage. Sixty-three of the 102 girls (62 percent) entered in the natural

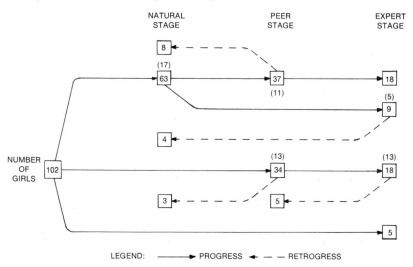

FLOW CHART SHOWING MOVEMENT OF 102 YOUNG WOMEN IN THE PRESCRIPTION PROCESS.

stage. Thirty-seven of these went on to the peer prescription stage and 18 of these went on to the expert stage. At the time of data collection, 17 of the 63 were still in the natural stage, 11 were still in the peer prescription stage, and the 18 who had progressed to the expert stage were still there. A less common pattern is illustrated by nine of the 63 who entered the process in the natural stage, but skipped the peer prescription stage and went into the expert stage. Of these nine, five were still in the expert stage and four had retrogressed to the natural stage.

The second most common pattern is skipping the natural stage and entering the prescription process in the stage of peer prescription. Thirty-four of the 102 girls (33 percent) did this. Of these, 18 went on to the expert stage. At the time of data collection, 13 were still in the peer prescription stage and three had retrogressed to the natural stage.

The least common pattern is entering the expert prescription stage directly. The five (5 percent) who did were still in this stage at the time of data collection.

A total of 20 of these girls—20 percent of the original number—retrogressed. Retrogression took place from the stage of peer prescription and from the stage of expert prescription. It did not take place in the most common pattern, where the girl progressed from the natural stage to the peer prescription stage and then to the expert stage, or in the least common pattern where the girl entered the prescription process in the expert stage. This indicates that awareness that has a chance to increase throughout the prescription process and awareness that is at the highest level at the start of sexual activity, as evidenced by the use of an expert method of birth control, are most conducive to maintaining the use of an expert method.

CHAPTER VI

Pregnancy, Abortion, and the Prescription Process

PREGNANCY: A CONSEQUENCE

Pregnancy is a possible consequence of the prescription process. It occurs in all stages of the process. Pregnancy in the expert stage was discussed in Chapter IV. In the natural and peer stages it occurs for the very reasons that girls are in those stages: infrequency of coitus and lack of knowledge:

> I didn't have sex that often, and I didn't know that much about birth control devices.

unexpectedness, lack of awareness, decision to abstain, and parents:

> The first time I did it I didn't think I'd do it again. The second time it just happened. I didn't think about birth control at those times. I only had sex a couple of times. Then I decided to abstain until I could handle the responsibility of a baby, but by that time I was pregnant. I knew about birth control. I have girlfriends who are taking pills. I couldn't go to my mother or father because they are strict Catholics.

change in sex patterns—breaking off a relationship:

I quit taking pills nine months ago when I broke up with my boyfriend. I just had sexual intercourse one time. It was unexpected. I was planning to get pills. I had an appointment already when this happened.

decision to abstain, inexperience with men, religion:

Perhaps I am a bit stupid. I could have sworn that I wouldn't have intercourse again. Looks like I was wrong. I guess people don't realize their weaknesses as much as they realize their strengths. I have not messed around with men much. I didn't get birth control because I used to be a devout Catholic and was against birth control and abortion. Every time I went to bed with a man I'd figure I wasn't going to do it again.

anticipated side effects:

I heard of the pill. I read about it. I didn't want to take it because I didn't want to get cancer. I didn't know about foam.

lack of parental consent:

I was scared to go see my doctor because I needed my parents' consent and my folks would guess permissiveness on my part.

lack of awareness and self-concept problem:

It just never sunk into my head that I might get pregnant.

inconsistency:

> We usually used condoms, but I don't know whether
> we were using one at the time I got pregnant.

reliance on the boy:

> God knows why I didn't use a birth control method.
> My boyfriend promised that everything would be all
> right and I foolishly believed him.

unexpected coitus:

> I didn't use anything because I was lonely. My
> boyfriend is overseas and it just seemed to happen. I
> was in the right place at the right time.

Pregnancies also occur in the transition period between
stages in the process. This is the time after an increase in
frequency of coitus triggers a girl to obtain an expert method
and before she actually obtains one. If the method is an oral
contraceptive, the lag is further prolonged by the time gap
between the actual date of the expert prescription and the date
when the preventive action of the pill takes effect. A girl may
conceive while awaiting an appointment with the doctor, or
even if she already has an oral contraceptive:

> I got the pill and had to wait until my next period to
> begin taking it, but my next period never came. I
> never got a chance to use it. Right after I received the
> pill, before I got a chance to use it, I conceived.

In some cases no birth control method was in use at the time of conception, but in others a peer prescription method was still in use.

Faulty communication between the girl and her expert consultant may result in transition period pregnancies. An example of faulty communication would be an expert's failure to tell the girl when a contraceptive's effectiveness begins: "I just got on the pill and they didn't tell me it wasn't safe at the beginning." Or a girl may not have been told exactly on which days she is to take the pills so that a pregnancy occurs due to "wrong counting of days."

PREGNANCY: A PROPELLENT

Pregnancy is a major propellent in the prescription process as well as a possible consequence. Whatever are the immediate circumstances of a pregnancy, it forces contact with the expert. If abortion is chosen, that may be the occasion for the first experience with the expert. The same is true of prenatal care or the delivery of a baby. The other types of pregnancy encounter —pregnancy of a friend or a pregnancy scare—also have this effect. Thus, pregnancy is one of the major triggers for seeking consultation with an expert.

ABORTION

Abortion can be used as a planned method, as was discussed in Chapter IV, or as an emergency method to prevent the consequence of an unwanted and unexpected conception that occurred in the course of the prescription process. Abortion is then considered the best solution because of financial and emotional conditions:

> I feel that having a baby now would spoil chances of living the way I want to live or would want a child to live.

Giving the baby up for adoption would be "more trouble and hassle" than an abortion and "you wouldn't want to give the baby up for adoption after all that." Many girls are concerned with the moral aspects of abortion and believe it is wrong to terminate a life, but others feel differently:

> ... life begins when a child is born and there is nothing wrong with abortion. It is not a life and you are not taking anything away from anyone, [so] the two people involved should decide.

Some girls feel it is "wrong to embarrass people like your parents," or "wrong to bring a child into the world without proper care and clothing," or that it is "more of a sin to deprive a child than to have an abortion." Although parents who are informed about a daughter's pregnancy will often give her financial and emotional support, it is common for girls to be afraid to disclose their plight to their parents. One girl said, "My mother would die and my father would kill me." This is a common reason for choosing abortion rather than keeping the baby or letting it be adopted.

A common fear about abortion is its possible effects on future fertility. Although some girls feel they will never want a family, others realize that they may desire children later on.

The time immediately after an abortion is a special case of transition, for then a birth control method has to be acquired. There is bound to be a time lapse between the abortion and effective use of birth control. Although sexual intercourse is usually avoided during this period, there is the possibility that the influences that first caused the girl to become pregnant will again take over, resulting in a repetition of her history in the prescription process: she returns to the natural stage because there seems to be no immediate prospect of sexual intercourse or because she has resolved to abstain from intercourse. In either case, a repeat pregnancy is possible. After an abortion, one young woman had intercourse once, using the rhythm method:

> I already had the pill. But after one intercourse I got pregnant. I have the prescription and the pill. Oh, no!

Just as some girls enter the other stages without purposeful intent—the natural stage because of low levels of awareness or the peer prescription stage because of reliance on the sex partner to supply a contraceptive—so may the expert stage be arrived at without purposeful intent because of a pregnancy. There will be various levels of awareness at this point, depending on the girl's history in the process. Many of the problems that existed previously are forced to a resolution: awareness is raised, self-concept is changed, sexual activity is disclosed, and contact is made with an expert. All this will influence the girl's future career in the prescription process. Successful birth control use is one subsequent outcome, but it is not the only outcome because many of the same conditions that were operable throughout the process are still present. Some of them are the same as those that were discussed in the section on abortion as a special case of transition. In addition, parents may be opposed to their daughter using a contraceptive. A girl who was seeking information for her second abortion said:

> My mother didn't want me to get birth control after my first abortion. I think she'll let me this time.

An expert method of birth control that is acquired after a pregnancy may be discontinued if there are adverse side-effects. When contact and interaction with an expert is maintained, shifting to another expert method is likely. Fear of side-effects may be allayed by a discussion with an expert, but when contact is not maintained, fear prevails and the method is discontinued.

When pregnancy occurs as a result of discontinuing a method because of its adverse side-effects, the experience may outweigh the side-effects, and the method that caused the side-effects may be resumed after the pregnancy because of its greater effectiveness. A typical pattern is the use of peer-prescribed methods followed by the use of an oral contraceptive which produces an undesirable side-effect. The oral contraceptive will then be discontinued and perhaps foam or another less effective method will be substituted. A pregnancy may result. Then the pill may be resumed. The resumption of the oral contraceptive may be based on greater experience and knowledge or a willingness to experience side-effects that are temporary in a determined effort to prevent another pregnancy. Experience and knowledge are acquired by going through the prescription process. This leads to exploration of other pill brands and dosages and new patterns of use that may alleviate the conditions that produced the side-effects. An example of changing a pattern of use is taking the pill at bedtime instead of in the morning, to prevent nausea. Increased experience may also lead to the realization that some side-effects are temporary and that the discomfort will disappear after an adjustment period. This may require the willingness to endure such side-effects as cramps and nausea for a period of time. As one young woman said:

> I did take pills, but stopped taking them because they made me sick. After this abortion I plan to go to my doctor and get them again.

Even in cases where the adverse effects of the pill indicate permanently discontinuing them, as in the case of the girl with thyroid and gynecological problems cited earlier, young women may be willing to risk possible serious consequences in order to avoid pregnancy. If a girl is unwilling to do this or does not acquire the experience and knowledge required for resuming the discontinued method, she may have repeated pregnancies.

If a pregnancy occurs as the result of discontinuing a method because of anticipated side-effects rather than experienced side-effects, the discontinued method will be resumed more easily. Although a repetition of the discontinuance-pregnancy-resumption pattern is possible, the chances of it are lower when anticipated rather than experienced side-effects are the reason for discontinuing a method.

CHAPTER VII

Birth Control – Toward a New Perspective

What is actually known about the birth control behavior of young, unmarried women and how has it been explained in the past? A review of the literature shows that there is a gap in research and knowledge in this area. In 1939, Kingsley Davis wrote:

> . . . illicit sexuality is a necessary, but not sufficient cause of illegitimacy. One could with more truth assert that the cause of illegitimacy is the *suppression of contraception and abortion.* . . . The sociological approach to the causation of illegitimacy attempts to show, in brief, that reproductive norms, whose violation constitutes illegitimacy, are broken . . . and that . . . illegitimate children are born of illicit relations because the measure that would prevent their being born (encouragement of contraception and abortion) constitute in themselves a violation of the mores. . . . Our taboos against contraception and abortion are at one with our taboo against extra-marital intercourse.

PAUCITY OF LITERATURE PRIOR TO 1970

Since Davis wrote this, a body of literature has grown up around the subject of premarital sexuality and illegitimacy, but there is no comparable body of literature on the use of contraceptives and abortion in the nonmarital context.

In an extensive review of the literature, Pohlman (1967a and 1967b) found that "compared to our knowledge of contraception within marriage and of pre-marital sex generally, our knowledge of pre-marital and extra-marital contraception is especially meagre." Of the studies that do exist, most are about knowledge and attitudes rather than actual behavior.

Zelnik and Kantner (1970) also note the lack of knowledge about contraception and abortion in the nonmarital situation. They say that most of our information on racial differences in fertility is with respect to married women in stable unions.

In one of the few studies prior to 1970 that gives some information on contraception in the premarital context, Schofield (1965) reports that initial premarital sex relations are typically unpremeditated and without contraception. Those with sex experience typically know of contraceptives, but so do those without such experience. Despite extensive fears of pregnancy, contraception is a surprisingly infrequent phenomenon among those having premarital sex. There is little evidence that knowledge of contraception encourages premarital sexual relations, or that fear of pregnancy is a major deterrent to such relations. The information on birth control behavior in the Schofield study was meager and only incidental to the study, which was concerned with sexual behavior in relation to venereal disease.

Contraceptive use has been correlated with various liaison levels ranged along a continuum of seriousness of the relationship, from intercourse with prostitutes to intercourse with fiancees (Kirkendall, 1961). The figures show that contraceptives were used in 58.1 percent of 668 premarital intercourse experiences on all liaison levels. The data indicates that contraceptive measures are more likely to be taken in relationships where thère is a definite degree of attachment than where there is little or no attachment. Although these data were collected from college-level males rather than from females (with which the present study is concerned), it is included because it is one of the few studies that reports findings on actual contraceptive use in an unmarried population.

There are many reports of the use of abortion among single women to prevent the birth of an unwanted child. The first such report to appear in the literature cites 363 cases of illegal abortions performed by two physicians. One hundred and two of the women were single and 81 were previously married (Tietze, 1949). It is interesting to note that, while the author discusses the implications of these abortions for the married women and says that, among them, abortions were "used primarily not as a method of child-spacing, but of limiting the ultimate size of the family," he says not a word about the implications of the abortions for the single women.

Other reports show that of 124 women treated for septic abortion at New York Hospital between 1953 and 1957, 64 percent were single women; that 56 abortion applicants from the United States arrived in Sweden in 1956, the majority of them unmarried 21- to 30-year-old women; that of 504 therapeutic abortions performed in Buffalo, New York, hospitals from 1943 to 1964, the percentage performed on unmarried women under the age of 20 increased over time; and that 77 percent of the therapeutic abortions performed in the Tampa General Hospital in a four-year period before 1967 were done for psychiatric indications in patients who were mostly white, single, or of good economic status (cited in af Geijerstam, 1969).

In a study of social network theory and abortion, of 114 women who had illegal abortions, 11 conceived with a fiance and 59 with a "serious" boyfriend (Lee, 1969).

While these studies show that unmarried women did at times take measures to prevent unwanted pregnancy, with the exception of the last study cited, they appeared in the medical literature and were not concerned with the sociological aspects of abortion or with abortion in the general context of birth control behavior. Furthermore, they were largely ignored by the behavioral scientists.

The literature on premarital sex is concerned with birth control only tangentially, if at all. The major concern of this literature is on deviation from sexual norms (Reiss, 1970b) and change in those norms.

In the literature on illegitimacy, birth control occupies a similar tangential position. A review of the major theoretical viewpoints toward illegitimacy (Roberts, 1966) cites two schools that have developed: (1) the psychological school that formulates explanations focused on intrapsychic factors within individuals, and (2) the social school. The three theoretical positions of the social school can be summarized under the rubrics of cultural relativism, cultural absolutism and cultural relationism. Roberts' review presents the works of 20 authors in 14 articles representing all of the aforementioned schools and theoretical positions. There are very few references to contraception and abortion.

Representing the psychological school in Roberts' review is Leontine Young (1945), who maintains that "one never finds a girl, however intelligent or educated, who has thought of contraceptives or has ever considered the possibility of an abortion as a solution to her problem" even in cases where she may be entitled to a therapeutic abortion. This is explained on the basis of the psychodynamic phenomenon that points to "the purposefulness of the girl's behavior, her determination, however unconscious, to have not just a baby, but specifically a baby out of wedlock."

That this point of view was prominent until very recently

is evident from an article in the social work literature in which Lipscomb (1969) advocates that:

> More attention must be paid by caseworkers to family planning, especially the dissemination of birth control information to women involved in relationships with men to whom they are not married. Illegitimacy is not always due to the psychodynamics of the mother, but sometimes to the lack of birth control measures and information available.

One of the three social school theories, the cultural absolutist theory, maintains that legitimacy is an absolute norm that is cross-cultural, and, like incest, under a universal and inviolate taboo. The only reference to contraception or abortion in the writings on this school which appear in Roberts' volume is that of Malinowski (1930), who says, "Contraceptives, I am firmly convinced, do not exist in Melanesia, and abortion is not sufficiently frequent to account for the great scarcity of illegitimate children." He hypothesizes that promiscuous intercourse reduces fertility.

The second social school theory, that of cultural relativism, maintains that illegitimacy, like many other social phenomena, is subject to the value system of the group within which it occurs and that various cultural groups may not have norms opposed to illegitimacy (Roberts, 1966). Christenson (1960), a cultural relativist, compares illegitimacy in Utah, Indiana, and Denmark, and maintains that the legal abortions so easily obtained in Denmark contribute to greater sexual freedom there.

The third social school theory, the theory of cultural relationism, is explicated by C. E. Vincent, and this position is summarized by Roberts (1966) as follows: Although there is an absolute norm about legitimacy, the phenomenon is closely related to other norms as well. "That is, a society may, while holding negative sanctions against illegitimacy, at the same time maintain permissive norms about related behavior" (i.e., premarital sex), and that,

> ...furthermore, of those who are caught in the conflict and become pregnant out-of-wedlock, those who have the most social sophistication and resources are more likely to resolve the problem via the quasi-approved cultural solutions of abortion or adoption.

Two hypotheses of cultural relationism are formulated in Roberts' review that postulate the interconnectedness of permissive premarital intercourse, cultural beliefs about birth control, abortion and adoption, and incidence of illegitimacy.

Only two more references to contraception and abortion appear in Roberts' theoretical review. One is by Kinsey (1958) who, in discussing pregnancies among single women, says that "it is a medical mistake to believe that contraceptives were totally inadequate 40 years ago ..." and that "there are very few women in our histories who have not at some time used contraceptives of one form or another." He concludes the discussion on single women by stating that the "proportion of pre-marital conceptions resolved before marriage by induced abortion is 88 to 95 percent."

The last reference to contraception in Roberts' theoretical review is in the final article by Jane Kronick (1962).

> Parenthetically [and the word is hers], in the casework literature there seems to be a rather common assumption that the promiscuous girl uses contraception effectively and thus is not the unwed mother. This does not appear to have been estab-

lished. On the contrary, it seems likely that at least some of the women who are repetitive mothers of illegitimate children are promiscuous.

This not only reveals the gap in knowledge on birth control in the unmarried context, but also characterizes its place in the literature—parenthetical.

However much these studies contribute to knowledge of the causes and aspects of illegitimacy, they do not illuminate the place of birth control in the premarital context to any degree, and they ignore the suppression of contraception and abortion information that the excerpt from Davis given at the beginning of this section referred to. The cultural relationism theory and the two hypotheses derived from it hold the most promise for filling the gap in knowledge about birth control in the unmarried context, but a review of Vincent's book (1961) shows no discussion of contraception and only a single reference to abortion. This reference appears on a scale of asocialization-socialization of sexual behavior that ranges from "limited involvement in passionate petting, no pre-marital coition" to "have had one or more pre-marital pregnancies, and kept at least one of the children." The reference to abortion is an item in the middle of the scale: "have had a non-therapeutic abortion." There is no item about coitus with contraception on the scale.

EMERGENCE OF A LITERATURE

Only very recently has a consideration of birth control in the nonmarital context appeared in the literature.

Osofsky (1970) notes that, although there have been hypotheses attempting to explain out-of-wedlock pregnancies by blaming immorality, mental deficiency, cultural encouragement, and psychological and psychiatric reasons, as well as explanations of "society as the patient" and, more recently, poverty, there are almost no studies that have related out-of-wedlock pregnancies to the availability of contraceptives and counseling in the nonmarital context. Osofsky concludes that no one factor is completely responsible for the occurrence of teen-age out-of-wedlock pregnancies, but that counseling, sex and contraceptive information, and availability of contraception can reduce the number of undesired pregnancies.

Cutright (1971) also recognizes the paucity of literature on birth control when he says that illegitimacy rates represent the end result of sexual behavior, contraception, and abortion use. Our explanations for illegitimacy rely for the most part on changes in socioeconomic and demographic events in the population because direct measures of its causes are often unavailable. He analyzes previous explanations of illegitimacy and concludes that its causes are not to be found in the traditional psychological or social explanations:

> The major reason unmarried women do not use effective contraception is *because they are unmarried.*
> . . . Marital status is the most important determinant of access to contraception and thus of contraceptive use.

Evidence of the inaccessibility of birth control services to unmarried women appears in Ortho (1968) and in a publication of the Westinghouse Learning Corporation (1971). Cutright's solution to the problem is:

> . . . the initiation of public programs through which effective medically supervised contraception is made available without humiliation, or eligibility requirements based on age, marital or financial status. Such programs should be backed up by the availability of abortion on request.

Goldsmith, et al. (1972), in one of the first studies that included both pregnant and never-pregnant girls, showed that most of the girls, both pregnant and never pregnant, had used some contraception previously. The most effective methods (pill, IUD, and diaphragm) were used for every sex experience by five percent of the new never-pregnant patients coming to the clinic for contraception, by one percent of the girls in the group seeking abortion, and by three percent of the group of girls in maternity homes. The authors of the study concluded that there were "fundamental differences" between contraceptors, abortion seekers, and pregnant girls planning to keep their babies. Contraceptors took initiative in seeking out effective contraception while the others sought help only after pregnancy. The contraception group also showed more self-acceptance and a predisposition to feeling more positive about pregnancy prevention.

Zelnik and Kantner (1970) explored the use of contraceptives by unmarried black women. Although the women favored the availability and use of contraceptives in principle, they were often opposed to them in practice. This was because contraceptives suggest a degree of sexual readiness or wantonness with which they did not wish to be associated, and also because contraceptives dim the aura of romance and impulsiveness that is supposed to surround sex. The study concludes that when socioeconomic status and education are held constant, blacks are more likely than whites to engage in premarital intercourse; less likely to use contraception; more likely to conceive; less likely to alter the outcome by abortion, falsification of legitimacy, or marriage; more likely to be regarded as independent by their parents; and, finally, likely to feel that a child born out of wedlock has as good a chance in life as any legitimate child of their race.

In a pretest pilot study, the same researchers (Zelnik and Kantner, 1972) compared white and black, unmarried, never-pregnant 15- to 19-year old girls with previously pregnant girls in the same age group. They found that more blacks had experienced intercourse than whites, but that blacks who had had sexual intercourse did not appear to be more sexually active then whites who had had sexual intercourse—in fact, the frequency of intercourse was higher for whites. Blacks had their first sex experience at an earlier age than whites. The black-white differential on pregnancy was the same as the black-white differential on experience of intercourse. Most blacks (82 percent) and whites (90 percent) used contraceptives, and contraception was started at the same age for both races. But whites tended to contracept sooner after first coitus, while blacks tended to start contracepting after a pregnancy. Delayed use of contraception by blacks contributed to the pregnancy differential. Whether because of delayed onset of contraception or irregularity or ineffectiveness of use, a number of blacks who used contraception also became pregnant.

METHODOLOGICAL ISSUES

The emerging literature on birth control in the nonmarital context has been patterned after the literature on marital fertility. In a discussion of some methodological issues in fertility, family planning, and the social organization of family life, Cicourel (1967) argues for a shift in research method and perspective. Without denying the relevance of standard economic, demographic, biological, and attitudinal factors, he feels there should be a shift in method and perspective so that the focus is on the routine, commonsense, expected, background features of everyday life and everyday rationality.

This shift in the method of research is needed for several reasons. One is that the general social context of family life and its articulation with family planning or absence of planning or objection to planning has not been examined seriously by social scientists. A second reason is the need for a conceptual way of showing the extent to which people's actions are guided by their perceptions and interpretations of the social structure. A third reason is that qualitative material enables us to assign meaning to presumed objective material. A fourth reason is that qualitative material and a research approach in which there are no preconceived categories permit categories based upon daily activities and decision-making procedures to be established. This is necessary for a comparative analysis of fertility and relevant social organization. A fifth reason is that coding operations (putting information into categories) and tabular presentations of findings become sociological, self-fulfilling prophecies unless the researcher knows how practical decisions that people make are related to the social setting in which the decisions are made and how they are related to the rules people use for making sense of their activities. Hilmar (1970) supports this contention. In discussing the need for descriptive data, he says:

> ... we need the kind of scholarly analysis and speculation that can assure that demographic trend data will not be misinterpreted and lead to overly simplistic and self-defeating policies.

McKinlay (1970) points out that the

> ... difficulty with most studies ... is that few of them consider how specific individuals and groups make a particular decision or why they opt for one form of behavior rather than another.

And Clausen (1967) says that

> ... indeed, one of the major deficits in our knowledge derives from the fact that research has overwhelmingly dealt with outcome variables and not with how the outcomes come about.

A NEW PERSPECTIVE

The birth control prescription process is grounded on the everyday rationality used in solving the practical problems of everyday life. The experiments in the peer prescription stage are examples of practical solutions to practical problems as they occur at a particular time in the lives of people. The birth control prescription process provides a perspective on behavior, a stance toward data; in short, a conceptual foothold toward an understanding of birth control behavior in the nonmarital context. This stance toward data and the qualitative material from which they are derived serves to integrate other research in the field and enables us to assign meaning to presumed objective material. For example, in the Zelnik and Kantner (1972) study, data are presented on the differences in frequency of inter-course between groups in the study. Current sexual activity is measured by frequency of intercourse "in the past month." Modal frequency was found to be zero for blacks and one to two times for whites. The prescription process brings a new depth of meaning to such data when it shows that an increase or decrease in the frequency of coitus is strongly related to the use or nonuse of contraceptives even when a girl has been sexually active and in the prescription process for a considerable time. A researcher familiar both with the prescription process theory and with the Zelnik and Kantner study would quickly see that the effects of social process need to be considered in the study of ethnic difference. Only by this type of study can we discern whether the differences in contraceptive use are due to social process or ethnicity.

In addition to adding meaning to single variables such as frequency of coitus, the prescription process theory allows for the patterning of variables. For example, in the study by Goldsmith, et al. (1972), three groups of unmarried girls are described: the contraception group, consisting of never-pregnant, new patients at the clinic; the abortion group, consisting of new patients seeking abortion counseling; and the maternity group, consisting of girls living at two maternity homes. The abortion and maternity groups were shown to differ from the contraceptive group on birth control use, educational goals, and marital goals. They used all methods of contraception less, their aims were to marry sooner after high school, and they sought less post-high school education. This shows a relationship of educational and marital goals to birth control behavior. In addition, they agreed with the following questionnaire items more frequently than the contraception group did: "I felt like a pregnancy would never happen to me," and, "I felt I shouldn't have intercourse at all, so I didn't plan ahead to do it or to use birth control." In the prescription process, these two items are related to awareness, self-concept, and ambivalence toward premarital sex. In the Goldsmith study these two items are analyzed and discussed separately from marital and education goals. But if all the differences in goals and questionnaire items are considered as a pattern from the perspective of the prescription process, an additional meaning is disclosed: that the girls in the abortion and maternity groups cannot conceive of sex and pregnancy in a nonmarital context, and that it is this lack of self-concept, low level of awareness, and ambivalence about premarital sex, together with their expressed goal of marriage, in which sexual behavior would be sanctioned, that is the source of their birth control behavior. In other words, sex is identified with marriage, not with development, and pregnancy is identified with marriage, not with sex. The result is that even though these girls are sexually active, they have no concern with the implications or consequences of their sexual activities at all, or they perceive marriage, not contraception, as the solution to the problem.

Such an attitude certainly has implications for population policy. One of the suggestions for reducing births is to legally postpone marriage (Davis, 1967). This reflects an identification of sex with marriage similar to that of the girls just discussed.

But postponing marriage does not necessarily postpone sexual activity. The analysis presented here indicates that the proposal may have an effect opposite to the one desired.

Since the prescription process theory was generated without preconceived categories, the categories established in the course of the research were based on the behavior and experiences of the people involved. That this makes comparative analysis possible can be shown by comparing two studies. Referring again to the Goldsmith, et al. (1972) and the Zelnik and Kantner (1972) studies, we see that in the former study the presentation of data on previous use of contraceptive methods yields a great deal of information on what, in terms of prescription process categories, would be the peer prescription stage. It is shown that higher rates of use of methods characteristic of this stage are associated with lower rates of pregnancy. There are no data on delayed use of contraceptives of any kind from the time of first coitus, that is, no data on a natural stage. Zelnik and Kantner refer to delayed use only, without designating the kinds of contraceptives that were used once contraception was begun. From the data in the prescription process study we know that it would be difficult to compare actual sequences of methods used because they are too numerous. But the use of natural and peer prescription stages as categories would enable the comparison of data from these two studies. Eventually enough information would accumulate to show how much pregnancy is avoided by activity in the peer prescription stage. This indicates that categories derived for a substantive theory such as the prescription process theory can be useful and relevant categories for the collection of data which can integrate other research in the field by making comparative analyses possible.

Coding operations and tabular presentations of findings become sociological, self-fulfilling prophecies unless practical decision-making in relation to social structure settings is articulated with rules people use for making sense of their activities. The following data from the 1972 Goldsmith, et al. study summarizes previous contraceptive use by three groups. Group I was composed of never-pregnant, first-time patients at a birth control clinic, Group II of young women seeking abortions, and Group III of maternity home residents who planned to carry their pregnancies to full term:

Method	Group I	Group II	Group III
Withdrawal	61	49	35
Condom	45	34	35
Rhythm	30	28	14
Douche	10	18	12
Foam	12	12	6
Pill	13	11	8

The authors' conclusion based on these findings was:

> . . . our findings are similar to those in many studies: girls who become pregnant have usually made little attempt to contracept and those who avoid pregnancy have tried a variety of methods.

From the perspective of the prescription process, there is a much more meaningful interpretation of this data. All three groups used a variety of methods and all three groups made attempts to avoid pregnancy. Note that the rank ordering of methods is virtually the same for the three groups. This seems to indicate that, although at the time of data collection there were more young women in the contraceptor groups that had gone through the natural and peer stages and were now entering the expert stage, the young women in the other two groups were pursuing the same course of behavior. They were at a different place in the birth control prescription process. They became pregnant before arriving at the expert stage. In addition to this similarity, there are other specific similarities revealed in the data. One is that in all three groups the use of expert methods, represented by data on the pill, is minimal after approximately one year of sexual activity (duration of sexual activity is revealed by other data in the study). Another similarity is that all groups showed retrogression from the expert stage. Retrogression is shown by comparing previous expert method use (the pill) with use of expert methods (the pill, diaphragm, or IUD) since the last menstrual period.

	Group I	*Group II*	*Group III*
Percent of previous pill use	13	11	8
Percent of pill, diaphragm, IUD use since last menstrual period	5	1	3
Percent of retrogression	8	10	5

Eight percent of the contraceptor group retrogressed; ten percent of the abortion group retrogressed; and five percent of the maternity group retrogressed. Given the similarity of behavior by all three groups, it would seem that a conclusion that those who come to the clinic for contraception are contraceptors while the others are not is, indeed, a self-fulfilling prophecy.

Another issue, in addition to those just discussed, is the paucity of theories that allow for change (Glaser and Strauss, 1967). This is most important in applied social science (Gouldner, 1956). The theory of the prescription process is made more powerful as an explanation of behavior by embracing the question of change. It addresses the question of change on many levels. The first level of change is the ever-changing, everyday reality which is manifested in perceptual, interpretive, and behavioral changes and consequent changes in birth control needs. The second level of change is on the social level.

Although we are not sure (because of the paucity of research on birth control behavior in the nonmarital context), it may be safe to assume that the process of nonmarital birth control planning has changed and will continue to change. On the third level, consideration of the question of birth control in the nonmarital context implies a change in the norm from the one formulated by Davis (1939), which says that the taboo against contraception and abortion in the nonmarital context is as strong as the taboo on premarital sex, to a newly emerging norm that regards premarital sex permissively if it is carried on in a responsible manner that includes the use of a contraceptive to prevent unwanted pregnancy. In addition to the implications of a changing norm are the implications of the fact that much of the research is directed toward abetting this change and changing the social process. Changes in the prescription process theory itself, resulting from changes in the social process, is a fourth level of change. The theory is flexible and subject to change with new data and new experience. Change could be postulated in the direction of collapsing the process by dropping out the natural and the peer prescription stages so that only the expert prescription stage remains, and what is now the least common career in the prescription process will become the most common career in the future. All of these changes are interrelated so that a change on any one level causes changes on the other three levels.

Glaser and Strauss (1967) give the requirements of a sociological theory, which appear to have been met by the birth control prescription process theory. These requirements are: (1) to enable prediction and explanation of behavior; (2) to be useful in the theoretical advance of sociology; (3) to provide a perspective on behavior—a stance to be taken toward data; (4) to guide and provide a style for research on particular areas of behavior; and (5), which was discussed in the previous chapter, to be usable in practical applications and to give the practitioner an understanding and some control of situations.

CHAPTER VIII

About the Research
for This Book

THE RESEARCH SETTING

The field research for the birth control prescription process was conducted mainly among young women aged 13 to 26, although there were a few above and below these ages. Most of the girls were unmarried, since the emphasis of the study was on birth control behavior in the nonmarital context, but some married women in the same age range were included so that comparisons in birth control behavior could be made. There were girls who had never been pregnant, some who were pregnant at the time of data collection, and some who had been pregnant at some time in the past. Among the girls who had never been pregnant, some had never had intercourse and never used a birth control method, some had had intercourse and never used a birth control method, and some had used contraception. Of those who had used contraception, some had used peer type methods and some had used expert type methods. Girls who were pregnant at the time of data collection had similar birth control histories. Most of the pregnant women were seeking abortion information, but there were also some who were planning to keep their babies or give them up for adoption. The girls who had been pregnant at some time in the past were comparable to the now-pregnant group in birth control use and in the disposition of their pregnancies. Thus, in contrast to studies on birth control behavior derived from research in illegitimacy, a full range of behaviors in relation to all the possible outcomes was ensured for the research. The birth of babies, after all, is only one of the possible outcomes of nonmarital sexual intercourse.

The actual research took place in four types of locale. The first was a free clinic organized and administered by young people. It provided community-based services for special people, young people, and minorities without direct charges and without red tape or eligibility tests (Page, 1969; Schwartz, 1971; and Stoeckle, et al., 1972). The second type of medical care delivery service was the county public health youth clinics, which are fashioned after the free clinics (Minkowski, 1971). The third type was a hospital-based clinic for pregnant teen-agers that included an extensive, well-developed outreach program. The fourth type was schools. Two schools were used in the research. One was a public high school in an upper-class area in the Los Angeles metropolitan area, and the other was a free school, that is, a school that is not part of a government district but is, rather, a private institution designed for unorthodox approaches to education. This school was also located in the Los Angeles area.

The research locales were in various socioeconomic and ethnic areas and included white, black, and brown ethnic groups and a variety of socioeconomic statuses.

The data were collected over the two- and one-half-year period from May, 1968, to December, 1970. During this time, many changes took place in the delivery of birth control services to unmarried women. At the start of data collection, the free clinic was the only place in the Los Angeles area that dispensed these services with no restraints. During the two- and one-half-year period, public health youth clinics were opened and Planned Parenthood began to deliver services to unmarried girls. Also during this period, the Belous decision of September, 1969, made abortion legal in California. Where, previous to this decision, girls were given information about where to obtain a safe abortion in other countries, after it referrals for abortion were made locally.

In the course of the field work, approximately 2,500 people were observed and/or questioned.

THE RESEARCH METHOD

The method used to generate the substantive theory of the birth control prescription process is described in *The Discovery of Grounded Theory* (Glaser and Strauss, 1967).

A substantive theory is one that is developed for a substantive, or empirical, area of sociological inquiry such as birth control, death and dying, and delinquency. It differs from formal theory, which is developed for a formal or conceptual area of sociological inquiry such as deviant behavior, social mobility, or status passage.

A grounded substantive theory is generated from data collected in the problem area under consideration. This means that the categories and most of the hypotheses and concepts not only come from the data, but are systematically worked out in relation to the data during the course of the research. This differs from research that has as its purpose verification of hypotheses. In such research, the categories are selected prior to data collection and the hypotheses and concepts are derived from a pre-existing theoretical framework. The problems and hypotheses are formulated first and then tested empirically. But empirical research goes beyond the testing of hypotheses and verification of theory in that it also initiates theories and hypotheses based on empirical observations (Merton, 1957). In this study, the theory is derived from qualitative data about birth control and other pertinent behavior that were collected from young, unmarried women.

To collect the qualitative data on which the theory is based, the *phenomenological* and *participant observer* approach was used. This approach allows "the subjects to speak for themselves" (Bruyn, 1971). It also considers that individuals are influenced by what they perceive to be real. This consideration is essential to any birth planning research (Pearson, 1971).

Major Strategies of the Method

The major strategies of the method for generating a substantive theory from data are: (1) theoretical sampling; (2) constant comparative analysis; and (3) simultaneous collection, coding and analysis of data.

In theoretical sampling, the comparison groups are not chosen by preplanned design as in research studies that are designed for the verification of theory. Groups are chosen in the course of the research in order to answer research questions that arise in the process of the research. The choice of the first group is based on the investigator's interest in the problem area to be studied. Thereafter, the choice of groups is based on the emerging theory in order to help generate emerging categories, develop to the fullest extent as many properties of the categories as possible, and help relate categories to each other and to their properties. This differs from research for verification of hypotheses where the selection of groups and categories to be studied takes place prior to data collection.

Constant comparative analysis is the continuous comparison of data from these groups. The comparison takes place throughout the course of the research. Again, this differs from research for the verification of hypotheses in which data comparison takes place only after all the data has been collected.

The comparison takes place by the simultaneous collection, coding and analysis of data. These three tasks are intertwined and constitute a process which is continuous throughout the course of the research.

These strategies generate the two major elements of a theory: (1) conceptual categories and their conceptual properties; and (2) hypotheses or generalized relations among the categories. Working out the theory systematically in relation to the data insures that the theory with its categories and hypotheses is relevant to and has great explanatory power for the area under study.

In this research the first group chosen for investigation consisted of girls who were pregnant and seeking abortion information. The first research question that arose was: If the trigger (Zola, 1964) for these girls to come to a clinic for information about abortion is pregnancy, what is the trigger for nonpregnant girls to come to a clinic for contraceptives? This question led us to the second group, which we called the birth control rap session group. Most of the girls in this group had never been pregnant, but all sought contraception information. Inquiries about the triggers that had motivated this group led to information which established frequency of coitus as a property of the category called dimensions of sexual activity, and so on to the other categories of the prescription process that are discussed in the chapter on the natural stage. A return to the first group showed changes in this property (frequency of coitus) over time and that these changes influence birth control behavior. The same turned out to be true of other properties. The hypotheses and generalizations that were derived from the development of the category called dimensions of sexual activity appear in all three of the chapters on stages, but particularly in the chapters on the natural and expert stages.

After finding out which triggers propelled a girl to come to the clinic, the next question that arose was: What, if anything, had she done about birth control before she came to the clinic? This led to gathering data on contraceptive histories in the birth control rap session group, which led again to the pregnant group for comparison. The patterns of contraceptive use that emerged from the analysis of the data on contraceptive histories as they were collected from both groups led to the concept of stages.

Thus, the theory emerged as the data were collected, coded, and analyzed.

Incidents for many categories were being collected at the same time. For example, while the collection of data on sexual activity was going on, data were collected from which other categories emerged. The category of awareness emerged in the course of collecting data on delay on contraception from the time of first coitus. As the data were collected, each new incident was coded into a category and compared to other incidents that had already been coded into that category.

Data were collected by multi-faceted investigation, in which there are no limits to the techniques of data collection, the way the data are used, or the types of data acquired. No one kind of data on a category or technique for data collection is necessarily appropriate. Different kinds of data give the researcher different views of vantage points from which to understand a category and develop its properties. Data collected from different vantage points are called slices of data. Examples of slices of data in this study are the data collected from parents, boyfriends, and professionals. This adds to an understanding of the way these social relationships influence movement in the prescription process.

Another reason for this openness of inquiry is that, when obtaining data on different groups, the diverse structural conditions of the groups must be considered. Schedules, restricted areas, work tempos, the perspectives of people in different positions, and the availability of documents of different kinds will vary in each group. To succeed, it is necessary to be flexible in the means for collecting data from group to group. For example, some of the data for this study were collected by self-administered questionnaires. This technique was used in most of the groups where data were collected, but in a public health youth clinic in a Mexican-American area this technique was frowned on. In that case, data were elicited in rap sessions and recorded in writing during them, or retained by memory and recorded in writing after them.

QUESTIONNAIRE

1.   First name only ————————————————— 2. Age ———

3.   Have you ever used any of the following methods for preventing pregnancy? Please indicate the ones you have used by placing a check next to them on the following list:

     __ rhythm or safe period   __ foam
     __ condom or rubber   __ sponge
     __ withdrawal or pulling out   __ I.U.D. or coil or loop
     __ diaphragm   __ douche
     __ pill or oral contraceptive   __ other. Please specify ———
     __ jelly   __ none
     __ suppository

4.   Did you use any of the above methods to prevent pregnancy the first time you had sex?

     __ yes __ no __ haven't had sex yet

     If you've already had sex, when was the first time? (Like 1 month ago, 2 years ago, etc.) ————————————————————

5.   Are you using anything to prevent pregnancy at the present time? ____ yes ____ no ____ sometimes

     If you answered yes, which method are you using? ——————
     ——

6.   Have you ever been pregnant? ____ yes ____ no

     If yes, what happened? (Please check one)

     ———— had an abortion
     ———— had a miscarriage
     ———— gave up the baby for adoption
     ———— kept the baby
     ———— other. Please specify

7.   Write down any questions you have about birth control that you would like to rap about or have answered. Like anything that's been bugging you or that you have been wondering about. (Use the other side of the page).

Many different tools and techniques of data collection were used in this study, including participant observation, individual and group interviews, self-administered questionnaires and questionnaires administered by the researcher. The sample questionnaire included here can be used by counsellors and other practitioners to quickly assess individuals or groups of girls in terms of where they are and where they have been relative to intercourse and birth control.

CHAPTER IX

Practical Uses of the Theory

The old beliefs about birth control in the nonmarital context are giving way to new ones. The old norm, as formulated by Kingsley Davis (1939), says that the taboos against contraception and abortion in the nonmarital context are as strong as the taboo on premarital sex. The newly emerging norm accepts premarital sex if, among other understood conditions, contraceptives are used. A major goal, then, is to encourage sexually active, unmarried people to use contraceptives. Two major proposals have been advanced to further this goal. One is to establish sex education programs in schools,[1] and the other is to establish a network of family planning clinics in and outside of hospitals and to encourage unmarried persons, including minors, to use these facilities (Cutright, 1971).

What is needed is a comprehensive birth control planning program that would incorporate both of these two major proposals as well as gain the support of community organizations in encouraging the practice of birth control planning among unmarried women. Different types of programs involving a variety of practitioners would be set up for intervention at different stages of the prescription process, depending on what is needed at any given time in a specific area. Great flexibility would be needed so that programs could be easily changed with changing needs and conditions.

But intervention in the birth control process does not have

---

[1] For a review of the various approaches to school programs, see Simmons (1970).

to wait until comprehensive planning is a reality. Our knowledge of the prescription process can enhance efforts in immediate, short-range interventions as well as in the context of some future comprehensive plan.

The birth control prescription process specifies the stages and conditions that are accessible to change. It also makes it possible to predict what effect various interventions might have on the behavior of individuals and on the other parts of the system. For example, if, because of limited resources, a director of public health youth clinics decides to attend only to the contraceptive needs of those in the expert stage and to ignore both the problem of sexual adjustment and the kinds of intervention needed in earlier stages of the process, he or she may come to the conclusion that the need for abortion services will continue at their present level because pregnancies will continue to occur in the natural and peer stages. Or if, because of conditions in her school (Pohlman, 1968) or the unavailability of services, a teacher gives contraceptive information but no information on where to get contraceptives or expert advice, she may predict that, while peer prescription activity would increase, and possibly pregnancies as well, so would awareness and readiness to accept professional services when they are made available. The possibly erroneous prediction that interventions at any one stage or with any single variable would lead directly to lowering the number of pregnancies would be avoided, as would the conclusion that interventions of this type are failures because they do not seem to result in a reduced number of pregnancies. Since pregnancy is a definite possibility all through the prescription process, it seems reasonable to predict that the process itself will have to be changed before there is a change in the number of pregnancies. The ultimate goal, then, is the collapse of the process so that the natural and peer prescription stages are eliminated, and young women are able to acquire expert birth control services, including abortion, and are allowed to practice birth control without strain. To reach this goal, changes must take place not only in the behavior of young women but in other parts of the social structure that affect the prescription process. For example, a medical education which imparts to its students a knowledge of the prescription process, and particularly a knowledge of the meaning to girls of the pelvic examination, will help to reduce aversion to expert services.

In addition to providing a scheme for interventions in a birth control planning process that enables predictions to be made about behavior, the birth control prescription process encourages practitioners to avoid the "fallacy of the empty vessels" (Polgar, 1963) whereby new programs that are offered fail because customs already established are disregarded. A remedy for this is to be aware of the popular culture, including behavior and orientations, and to phrase one's message in terms of existing notions. The birth control prescription process provides a picture of the popular birth control culture in the nonmarital context, and includes sufficient specific instances to enable its messages to be delivered in terms that are acceptable to those to whom they are given. For example, in counseling a group of young women, it is far more effective to say, "I know a lot of you feel there is no chance of your getting pregnant, or that because you are having sex infrequently there is no need for birth control," than to tell them, "You need to face up to your responsibilities."

A sociological theory must be usable in practical applications and must give the practitioner an understanding and some control of situations (Glazer and Strauss, 1967). Four highly interrelated properties make it possible to use the theory of the birth control prescription process in practical situations: First, it fits the substantive area in which it will be used, which means that (a) it is not divorced from the everyday realities of the problems it is designed to influence, (b) it indicates how the theory relates to these problems, and (c) it indicates where and how to begin applying the theory. Second, it provides, in nontechnical and understandable language, an analytic framework for family planning personnel at the same time that it sensitizes by providing a meaningful picture with apt illustrations that planners can understand in terms of their own experience. Third, it is general enough to serve as a guide in the ever-changing situations that arise in the field of birth control planning in the nonmarital context. And fourth, it provides a conceptual, theoretical foothold in the realities of the situation, with variables that can be controlled, understood, and analyzed by the practitioner (Gouldner, 1959), who can then produce and predict changes in them, and, further, can predict and control consequences both for the object of change and for other parts of the total situation. At the same time, it is flexible and amenable to revision in tactics and even in the theory itself when the practitioner finds this necessary.

It is hoped that the theory of the birth control prescription process will, by providing these practical benefits, help the practitioners and young women who are already in the process of solving the problem of how to prevent unwanted pregnancies and birth in the nonmarital context.

References

af Geijerstam, G. K. 1969. An Annotated Bibliography of Induced Abortion. Ann Arbor: University of Michigan Press.

Barrett, J. C., and Marshall, J. 1969. The risk of conception on different days of the menstrual cycle. *Population Studies* 23:455-462.

Becker, H., and Geer, B. 1970. Participant observation and interviewing: a comparison. In Qualitative Methodology: Firsthand Involvement With the Social World, ed. W. J. Filsted, pp. 133-142. Chicago: Markham Publishing Company.

Bruyn, T. 1970. The new empiricists: the participant observer and phenomenologist. In Qualitative Methodology: Firsthand Involvement With the Social World, ed. W. J. Filsted, pp. 283-287. Chicago: Markham Publishing Company.

Chang-Silva, A. W.; Mudd, E. H.; and Garcia, C. R. 1971. Psychosexual response and attitudes toward family planning. *Obstetrics and Gynecology* 37:289-296.

Cherniak, D., and Feingold, A. 1970. Birth Control Handbook. Montreal: McGill Students' Society.

Christenson, H.T. 1960. Cultural relativism and premarital sex norms. In The Unwed Mother, ed. R. W. Roberts, 1966, pp. 61-77. New York and London: Harper and Row.

Cicourel, A. V. 1964. Method and Measurement in Sociology. London: Free Press of Glencoe.

Cicourel, A. V. 1967. Fertility, family planning, and the social organization of family life: some methodological issues. *Journal of Social Issues* 23:57-82.

Cimons, M. 1971. Midnight mugging—woman writer tells what it's like. *Los Angeles Times,* Part I, p. 1, Sept. 10, 1971.

117

Clausen, J. A. 1967. The organism and socialization. *Journal of Health and Social Behavior* 8:243-252.

Cogswell, B. E. 1967. Rehabilitation of the paraplegic: processes of socialization. *Sociological Inquiry* 37:11-26.

Coombs, R. H. 1968. Sex education for physicians: is it adequate? *Family Coordinator* 17:271-277.

Crist, T., and Starnes, L. 1972. Student printing presses bring birth control story to colleges: review of 12 books by college students. *Family Planning Perspectives* 4:60-61.

Cutright, P. 1971. Special feature: illegitimacy; myths, causes, and cures. *Family Planning Perspectives* 3:25-48.

Daniels, A. K. 1971. Sexual social types and the etiquette of sex relations. Paper read at P.S.A. meeting, April, 1971, Hawaii.

Davis, K. 1939. Illegitimacy and the social structure. *American Journal of Sociology* 45:215-233.

Davis, K. 1967. Population policy: will current programs succeed? *Science* 158:730-739.

de Beauvoir, S. 1952. The Second Sex. New York: Alfred A. Knopf.

Eastman, W. R. 1972. First intercourse. *Sexual Behavior* 2:22-27.

Elliott, R.; Landman, L. C.; Lincoln, R.; and Tsuoroka, T. 1970. U. S. population growth and family planning: a review of the literature. In The American Population Debate, ed. D. Callahan, pp. 185-226. Garden City: Doubleday and Company.

Family Planning Digest (*see* National Center for Family Planning, etc.)

Friedson, E. 1960. Client control and medical practice. *American Journal of Sociology* 65:374-282.

Friedson, E., 1961. Patients' Views of Medical Practice. New York: Russell Sage Foundation.

Furstenberg, F. F. Jr. 1969. The prevention of adolescent illegitimacy. Paper presented at the 64th Annual Meeting of the American Sociological Association, Sept., 1969.

Furstenberg, F. F. Jr. 1971. Birth control experience among pregnant adolescents: the process of unplanned parenthood. *Social Problems* 19:192-203.

Furstenberg, F. F. Jr.; Masnick, G. S.; and Ricketts, S. A. 1972. How can family planning programs delay repeat teenage pregnancies? *Family Planning Perspectives* 4:54-60.

Gabrielson, I. W. et al. 1971. Adolescent attitudes toward abortion: effects on contraceptive practice. *American Journal of Public Health* 61:730-738.

Glaser, B. G., and Strauss, A. L. 1967. The Discovery of Grounded Theory: Strategies for Qualitative Research. Chicago: Aldine Publishing Company.

Goldsmith, S. 1969. San Francisco's teen clinic: meeting the sex education and birth control needs of the sexually active schoolgirl. *Family Planning Perspectives* 1:23-26.

Goldsmith, S.; Gabrielson, M. O.; Gabrielson, I.; Mathews, V.; and Potts, L. 1972. Teenagers, sex, and contraception. *Family Planning Perspectives* 4:32-38.

Goldsmith, S. n.d. Communicating with teenagers about a contraceptive program. San Francisco: Planned Parenthood/World Population. Mimeograph.

Goodenough, W. H. 1963. Cooperation in Change. New York: John Wiley and Sons.

Gouldner, A. 1956. Explorations in applied social science. *Social Problems* 3:169-181.

Gouldner, A. 1959. Theoretical requirements of the applied social sciences. *American Sociological Review* 22:92-102.

Hardin, G. 1966. The history and future of birth control. *Perspectives in Biology and Medicine* 10:1-18.

Hilmar, N. A. 1970. Knowledge for what? Elegance and relevance in population and family planning research. *Family Planning Perspectives* 2:30-34.

Kantner, J. F., and Zelnik, M. 1969. United States: exploratory studies of Negro family formation—common conceptions about birth control. *Studies in Family Planning* 41:10-13.

Kimmey, J. R. 1971. Sex and the single-minded: education foes renew fight. *Nation's Health* 1:3.

Kinch, R. A. H.; Wearing, M. P.; Love, E. J.; and McMahon, D. 1969. Some aspects of pediatric illegitimacy. *American Journal of Obstetrics and Gynecology* 105:20-31.

Kinsey, A. 1958. Illegal abortion in the United States. In The Unwed Mother, ed. R. W. Roberts, 1966, pp. 121-123. New York and London: Harper and Row.

Kirkendall, L. A. 1961. Premarital Intercourse and Interpersonal Relationships. New York: Julian.

Knox, D. H. Jr. 1970. Attitudes toward love of high school seniors. *Adolescence* 5:89-100.

Kronick, J. C. 1962. An assessment of research knowledge concerning the unmarried mother. In The Unwed Mother, ed. R. W. Roberts, 1966, pp. 233-251. New York and London: Harper and Row.

Lee, N. H. 1969. The Search for an Abortionist. Chicago: University of Chicago Press.

Lipscomb, N. I. 1969. Casework and family planning. *Social Casework* 50:204-209.

Lowry, R. P. 1969. First coitus. *Medical Aspects of Human Sexuality* 3:91-97.

Malinowski, B. 1929. The Sexual Life of Savages. New York: Harcourt, Brace, and World, Inc.

Malinowski, B. 1930. Parenthood—the basis of social structure. In The Unwed Mother, ed. R. W. Roberts, 1966, pp. 25-41. New York and London: Harper and Row.

McCall's. 1972. Birth control in the high schools? *McCall's,* Jan. 1972, 59.

McKinlay, J. B. 1970. A brief description of a study on the utilization of maternal and child welfare services by a lower working class subculture. *Social Science and Medicine* 4:551-556.

Mechanic, D. 1968. Medical Sociology. New York: The Free Press.

Merton, R. K., and Kendall, P. L. 1955. The focused interview. In The Language of Social Research, eds. P. F. Lazarsfeld and M. Rosenberg, pp. 476-489. Glencoe: Free Press.

Merton, K. 1957. Social Theory and Social Structure. New York: The Free Press.

Minkowski, W. L.; Weiss, R.; and Heidbreder, G. 1971. The county of Los Angeles health department youth clinics. *American Journal of Public Health* 61:757-775.

Montagu, A. 1969. Sex, Society, and Man. New York: G. P. Putnam and Sons.

Muuss, R. E. 1970. Puberty rites in primitive and modern societies. *Adolescence* 5:111-128.

National Center for Family Planning Services, Health Services, and Mental Health Administration, U. S. Dept. of Health, Education, and Welfare.

1972. Teenage clinics meet urgent personal and social needs. *Family Planning Digest* 1:7-9.

Ortho Pharmaceutical Corporation. 1968. Ortho Panel 3: Teen-age and premarital sexual counseling. Cited by S. Goldsmith in San Francisco's teen clinics, *Family Planning Perspectives* 1:2:24.

Osofsy, H. J. 1970. Teenage out-of-wedlock pregnancy: some preventive considerations. *Adolescence* 5:151-170.

Page, L. 1969. The free clinic: if you need help, don't split. *Private Practice* 1:6-11.

Pearson, J. 1971. Review of The Psychology of Birth Planning by Edward Pohlman. *Journal of Biosocial Science* 3:341-346.

Pilpel, H., and Wechsler, N. 1969. Birth control, teenagers, and the law. *Family Planning Perspectives* 1:29-36.

Pilpel, H., and Wechsler, N. 1971. Birth control, teenagers, and the law: a new look. *Family Planning Perspectives* 3:37-45.

Pohlman, E. 1967a. The Psychology of Birth Planning. Cambridge: Schenkman Publishing Company.

Pohlman, E. 1967b. A psychologist's introduction to the birth planning literature. *Journal of Social Issues* 23:13-28.

Pohlman, E. 1968. Premarital contraception and the school. *Phi Delta Kappan,* May, 1968: 495-500.

Polgar, S. 1963. Health action in cross-cultural perspective. In Handbook of Medical Sociology, eds. E. Freeman, S. Levine, and L. G. Reeder, pp. 397-419. Englewood Cliffs: Prentice-Hall, Inc.

Rainwater, L. 1965. Family Design: Marital Sexuality, Family Size, and Contraception. Chicago: Aldine Publishing Company.

Rainwater, L. 1968. The lower class: health, illness, and medical institutions. In Among the People, eds. I. Deutscher and E. J. Thompson. New York: Basic Books.

Rainwater, L., and Weinstein, K. K. 1960. And the Poor Get Children. Chicago: Quadrangle Books.

Reiss, I. L. 1966. Contraceptive information and sexual morality. *Journal of Sex Research* 2:51-57.

Reiss, I. L. 1967. The Social Context of Premarital Sexual Permissiveness. New York: Holt, Rinehart, and Winston.

Reiss, I. L. 1970a. The influence of contraceptive knowledge on premarital sexuality. *Medical Aspects of Human Sexuality,* Feb.: 71-86.

Reiss, I. L. 1970b. Premarital sex as deviant behavior: an application of current approaches to deviance. *American Sociological Review* 35:78-87.

Reiss, I. L. 1972. The pill and adolescent sexuality. *Medical Aspects of Human Sexuality* 6:178.

Roberts, R. W., ed. 1966. The Unwed Mother. New York and London: Harper and Row.

Schofield, M. 1965. The Sexual Behavior of Young People. London: Longmans, Green.

Schwartz, J. L. 1971. First national survey of free medical clinics 1967-1969. *HSMHA Health Reports* 86:775-787.

Simmons, O. G. 1970. Population education: a review of the field. *Studies in Family Planning* 52:1-5.

Stoeckle, J. D.; Anderson, W. H.; Page, J.; and Breener, J. 1972. The free medical clinics. *Journal of the American Medical Association* 219:603-605.

Stycos, J. M. 1964. Population and family planning programs in newly developing countries. In Population, the Vital Revolution, ed. R. Freedman, pp. 166-177. New York: Doubleday and Company.

Thiebaux, H. J. 1972. Self-prescribed contraceptive education by the unwillingly pregnant. *American Journal of Public Health* 62:689-694.

Tietze, C. 1949. Report on a series of illegal abortions induced by physicians. *Human Biology* 21:60-64.

Tietze, C. 1970. Evaluation of intrauterine devices: ninth progress report of the cooperative statistical program. *Studies in Family Planning* 55:1-40.

Tietze, C., and Lewitt, S. 1969. Abortion. *Scientific American* 220:21-27.

Tillack, W. S.; Tyler, C. W. Jr.; Paquette, R.; and Jones, P. H. 1972. A study of premarital pregnancy. *American Journal of Public Health* 62:676-679.

Udry, J. R.; Clark, L. T.; Chase, C. L.; and Levy, M. 1972. Can mass media advertising increase contraceptive use? *Family Planning Perspectives* 4:37-44.

Vincent, C. E. 1961. Unmarried Mothers. Glencoe: Free Press.

Wadsworth, M.; Loudon, N.; Rankin, M.; and Herbert, I. 1971. Attenders at a contraceptive clinic for single women. *Journal of Biosocial Science* 3:133-143.

Westinghouse Learning Corporation. 1971. Family Planning for Teenagers. No. 6 in the Focus on Health Series, Health Services Division, Bladensburg, Maryland.

Wolf, S. R., and Ferguson, E. L. 1969. The physician's influence on the nonacceptance of birth control. *American Journal of Obstetrics and Gynecology* 104:752-757.

Young, L. 1945. Personality patterns in unmarried mothers. In The Unwed Mother, ed. R. W. Roberts, 1966, pp. 81-94. New York and London: Harper and Row.

Zelnik, M., and Kantner, J. F. 1970. United States: exploratory studies of Negro family formation—factors relating to illegitimacy. *Studies in Family Planning* 60:5-9.

Zelnik, M., and Kantner, J. F. 1972. Some preliminary observations on pre-adult fertility and family formation. *Studies in Family Planning* 3:59-65.

Zola, I. 1964. Illness behavior of the working class. In Blue-Collar World: Studies of the American Worker, eds. A. Shostak and W. Gomberg, pp. 350-361. Englewood Cliffs: Prentice-Hall.

Index